The Railway Children

E. Nesbit
adapted by
Dave Simpson

Samuel French – London
New York – Sydney – Toronto – Hollywood

FOR AMATEUR PRODUCTION ENQUIRIES

UNITED KINGDOM AND WORLD
EXCLUDING NORTH AMERICA

plays@SamuelFrench-London.co.uk

020 7255 4302/01

Each title is subject to availability from Samuel French,

depending upon country of performance.

THE RAILWAY CHILDREN

First presented by the Coliseum Theatre Company at the Coliseum Theatre, Oldham, on 3rd November, 1984, with the following cast of characters.

Roberta	Julia Ford
Phyllis	Gwendoline Begley
Peter	Stephen Clark
Mother	Ingrid Lacey
Perks	Colin Meredith
Mrs Perks	Brenda Elder
Old Gentleman	Alan Partington
Doctor Forrest	Nicholas Fry
Mr Szczepansky	Neil Caple
John	John Wolfenden
Alfred	James Swan
Bert	Peter Moore
Edith	Jenny Luckraft
Emma	Carolynne Jones
Joan	Zoey Holt
Jim	Jonathan Devaney
other parts played by	Alex Brown, Victoria Littler and members of the Company

Directed by Peter Fieldson
Designed by Judith Croft
Lighting designed by Tim Aspeling

CHARACTERS

Roberta
Peter } The Railway Children
Phyllis

Mother

Perks

Mrs Perks

John
Alfred
Edith } The Perks' Children
Bert
Emma
Joan

Mrs Walker

Doctor Forrest

Mr Szczepansky

District Superintendent

Old Gentleman

Jim

"Hounds"

Father

Passengers and passers-by

The action takes place in and around a country railway station

Time—the turn of the century

AUTHOR'S NOTE

In the original production at Oldham Coliseum the set was a revolve divided into three sections: the station and station house; the Three Chimneys Cottage and garden; the countryside.

In subsequent productions theatres have used a variety of sets to make the play work; these include trucking on and off the various sets. However, a composite set could also be used successfully. The device of having Perks narrating by his set of points and turning them for each set change seems to work very well no matter what set is used.

At the Oldham Coliseum the parts of Phyllis, Peter and John were all played by child actors. However, in other productions these have sometimes been played by young-looking professional actors.

Although the play is written in a Northern dialect the play is best served when the accents and local references are adapted to the particular region of the production. For instance, when the play was performed at the Northcott Theatre, Perks, his children and the locals all had Exeter accents.

Dave Simpson

ACT I

Perks can be seen through open waiting-room doors on the platform. There is steam everywhere. There is the silhouette effect of a train seemingly drawn up in the station

Perks All aboard for the eight forty-five to Leeds calling at Todmorden, Hebden Bridge, Mytholmoroÿd, Halifax, Sowerby Bridge, Bradford, and Putney. (*He blows his whistle*)

The train begins to pull out. Perks comes through the doors, closing them behind him. He moves to the points downstage

Oh, hello. I don't reckon that the three kids we called the Railway Children could ever have dreamed how important this 'ere station were going to be to their lives. (*He continues to work*) See, at first, when their story begins, they were living in London. Right posh they were an' all. Loaded wi' money. There was their mam and dad, and Phyllis who they called Phyl, Peter, and of course Roberta, who they called Bobbie. Their story really starts one evening when there was a knock at their door and these two big fellahs stood there. They wanted to see their dad and they spent about half an hour chatting to him before he went off with 'em. Well, their mam was right upset I can tell you, though she didn't let on to the three kids. And about a month later when Dad still hadn't come back Mam told 'em that he'd gone away on business—government business—and he'd be away for some time. And worst of all, for a while anyroad, they hadn't much money and they had to sell up and move to a small cottage up 'ere. And that's wha' happened. Late one night, after a long journey, they arrived at my station.

Mother, Roberta, Phyllis and Peter enter. Mother carries suitcases

Mother Well . . . here we are, my lovelies.
Peter Are we getting a cab?
Mother Peter, you won't find any cabs in the country.
Peter No cabs?
Mother I'm afraid we're going to have to walk.
Phyllis But it's so dark. And where are the gas lamps?
Mother No gas lamps either, Phyl. Not in the country.
Phyllis No gas lamps?
Mother No, darling. Now come on, the walk won't take us long.
Peter I'll carry the heaviest case if you like, Mother.
Mother That's all right, Peter. You take this one.

Phyllis I'm tired, Mummy.
Mother We'll soon be at the cottage, my lovely, then we'll have a nice meal and you can go straight to bed. Isn't this exciting?
Phyllis It's ever so dark, Mummy ... and there's no-one about.
Mother That's because it's very late.

An owl hoots

Phyllis Oooo ... what was that?
Mother An owl.

The owl hoots again

Roberta Take my hand, Phyl.
Phyllis Isn't it quiet?
Peter I'm not frightened of the dark. You can all follow me if you like.
Mother Peter, do you know where you're going?
Peter Er, yes.
Mother Where?
Peter Er ... over here.
Mother No. It's this way, darling.
Peter Oh ... yes, well that's what I thought.
Mother Come on.
Phyllis Oh, just a minute, my bootlace has come undone.
Peter Not again!
Mother Isn't this a beautiful night? Much nicer than the smelly old town, isn't it?

Mother, Roberta and Peter move off

Phyllis is tying her bootlace

Phyllis Wait for me!

Phyllis dashes off after her family

Perks changes the points and the set changes to the cottage

Perks And it wasn't long before they reached the Three Chimneys Cottage. It doesn't take much brain power to see why it were called Three Chimneys, does it?

Perks exits

Mother (*off*) You see, we're here already. That wasn't so bad was it?
Peter (*off*) It's not very big.
Mother (*off*) It's big enough for us. Mrs Viney said she'd leave the key under the door step. Ah. You see.

Mother opens the door and enters, followed by Peter, Roberta and Phyllis

Peter Oh, isn't it spooky?
Phyllis I can't see anything.
Peter Ooooooooooooo!

Phyllis jumps

Mother Stop it, Peter.
Peter I was only joking.
Phyllis Horrid boy!

There is a scurrying sound

Children What was that!?
Mother I expect it'll only be some poor little field mice.
Children Field mice!
Phyllis Only field mice!
Mother They'll be as frightened as you are. Now—shall we have some light?
Phyllis Yes, please!
Mother Now ... candles ... ah ... Mrs Viney's left us two on the table.
Peter Is there no gas light?
Mother I'm afraid not, darling.
Phyllis And it's so cold, Mummy.
Mother We'll light a fire later. (*She lights a candle*) Isn't this fun?
Roberta Yes.
Mother It's quite an adventure, isn't it? There.
Peter Oh, it's so gloomy in here.
Phyllis And there aren't any curtains or carpets.
Mother We can sort that out tomorrow, can't we?
Roberta I think it's a lovely little cottage, Mother.
Mother I think so too. Now—are we all hungry?
Children Oh yes.
Mother Good. I asked Mrs Viney to get us some bread and meat and things for supper. I expect she's laid it out in the dining-room. Maybe you'd all like to go and find it.
Phyllis In the dark?
Mother I'll give you a candle. Have a search round the house. Like an adventure.

Mother hands Roberta the candle. They do not see there is a tray covered up on one of the chests

Phyllis (*frightened*) I'll go with Roberta.
Peter Oh ... in that case, I'll go ... with Roberta as well.

Roberta, Peter and Phyllis exit

Mother lights another candle

Phyllis (*off*) They weren't really field mice, were they?
Peter (*off*) No, they were probably rats.
Roberta (*off*) Peter!
Phyllis (*off*) There's no carpet in here either ... just flagstones.
Mother Have you found it, children?
Roberta (*off*) It's not in here.

Mother lights another candle

Mother Oh dear. What a terrible thing to do. She's just walked off with the money and not got us anything to eat at all.

Roberta, Peter and Phyllis enter

Phyllis Then shan't we have any supper?
Mother Oh yes. Only it'll mean unpacking one of those chests we sent on.
Roberta Where?
Peter Over there. (*He begins dragging the chest across the floor*)
Roberta Shall I help you, Peter?
Peter (*indignantly*) No, I can manage quite well, thank you very much.
Roberta I'm sure you can, but I'll help you all the same.

They drag it into the light

Peter It's locked.
Mother Yes, it's been nailed down.
Peter Where's the hammer?
Mother I'm afraid it's inside the box.
Phyllis What are we going to do then?
Mother Get that coal shovel over there—and the poker.

Peter does so

  I'm sure we'll be able to manage. (*To Peter*) Thank you.
Roberta Do be careful, Mummy.

Mother tries to prise open the lid with little success

Peter Let me do it.
Mother I can manage.
Roberta Mind you don't hurt your hands.
Phyllis I wish Father were here, he'd get it open in two shakes.

Roberta kicks Phyllis

  What are you kicking me for, Bobbie?
Roberta I wasn't.

The chest creaks open

Mother Here we are. You see. No trouble.
Phyllis I think that Mrs Viney's a horrible woman not to leave us any
  supper.
Mother I'm glad I packed all the odds and ends out of the store cupboard.
Roberta Here's a tablecloth.
Peter And some knives and forks.
Roberta I'll set the table.
Peter I'll help you.

The children start to set the table

  Some more candles here, Mummy.
Mother Oh good. You can light a candle each. I think you'll find some
  saucers in there as well. Just drop a little candle-grease in the saucer and
  stick the candle upright in it. But be very careful.
Phyllis Oh, can I light one too?
Mother As long as you're careful.

The children start to light the candles

Roberta This is much more fun than gas light.

Phyllis strikes a match and burns herself

Phyllis Ohhhhh! I've burnt myself.
Mother Are you all right, darling?
Roberta Let me see, Phyl. Oh, it's only a little burn. If you'd been a Roman martyr you would've been burnt whole if you'd happened to live in the days when those things were fashionable.
Phyllis Oh, how horrid. I wouldn't have liked that at all.
Mother I'm sure you wouldn't. There. Now doesn't this look much cosier?
Roberta What have we got for supper, Mummy?
Mother Well—I think it's going to be quite the oddest supper we'll ever eat in our lives. (*Taking out the contents*) Marie biscuits ... sardines ... preserved ginger ... cooking raisins and candied peel and marmalade.
Peter (*screwing up his nose*) Ooooooohhhhh!
Roberta I think it sounds delicious.
Mother Well—maybe not delicious—but it'll have to do.

The table is laid, and the supper prepared

Don't put the marmalade spoon in among the sardines, Phyl.
Phyllis No, Mummy.
Roberta Where are the plates?
Mother I think you'll find them in the corner of the packing case wrapped in paper.
Roberta Here's some ginger wine.
Mother Oh lovely—this is going to be quite a feast after all.
Roberta Have we any glasses, Mummy?
Mother Let's use the willow pattern teacups for now. Can you see them?
Roberta They're here.
Mother Open the ginger wine, Peter.

Peter does so

Hold up your cups.

Peter fills them

Lovely. And let's toast to our new home. To our Three Chimneys Cottage.
All To our Three Chimneys Cottage.

They all drink

Phyllis Oh, I do wish Daddy were here.

Mother puts her arm round Phyl. A train is heard

What was that?
Mother Only a train.
Peter (*turning*) Oh look.

The children rush to the window

Roberta It looks like a toy engine from here, Peter.
Peter Oh yes!
Roberta It's so small and dark. Almost like a ghost train.
Peter Tomorrow we must go down the railway and have an explore.
Roberta Yes, we must.
Phyllis I wonder who's on it?
Roberta Lots of people I expect.
Phyllis Maybe Father!
Roberta (*gently*) Don't be silly, Phyllis.
Phyllis I'm not being silly. Mother, could it be Father?

A moment

Mother Come and finish your supper, darlings. You must be very hungry.

They return to the table. Roberta pushes Phyllis for being tactless

Phyllis Don't do that.
Mother You see it is an exciting place to be, isn't it, children?
Phyllis I'm not hungry any more.
Mother You must eat something, Phyl. At least have a biscuit. Here.
Phyllis No thank you, Mummy. (*She knocks over the bottle of ginger wine*)
Mother Oh Phyl.
Peter Look what you've done, you clumsy clot.
Mother (*chiding gently*) Peter ...
Phyllis It wasn't my fault it's so dark in here.
Mother Look, Phyl, there's a tea towel on the chest there, go and get it and
    we'll mop it all up. There's no harm done.
Phyllis (*moving*) It's not my fault there isn't any gas light.
Roberta Phyllis ...
Phyllis Well, it isn't ... (*She takes off the tea towel covering the food tray on
    the chest*) Oh Mummy!
Mother What's the matter, darling?
Phyllis This tray is full of food. Lots of lovely, lovely food. Look!
Mother Oh yes! Bring it over here darling.

Phyllis brings it over

Mother Well I never.
Children Ooooooo!
Mother Now doesn't this look delicious? And all those awful thoughts I had
    about Mrs Viney. Look children, she's done us proud!

Mother and children gather round the food

  Perks enters downstage and changes the points

The set changes to the station

  Mother and children exit

Perks And so began their lives at Three Chimneys Cottage. The following morning, bright as three new pennies, they came down to the station.

Perks looks at his pocket watch. Sounds of an approaching train are heard

Perks goes out through the centre doors and the train is heard coming to a halt

(*Off*) All aboard for the ten thirty-four to Manchester.

Roberta, Peter and Phyllis enter the ticket office

The train pulls out

Perks comes back through the centre doors, changes his hat and becomes the ticket collector. Passengers start to pass through the station beginning with a Man

Man Morning, Mr Perks.
Perks Morning, Mr James.
Man Fine morning.
Perks Beautiful.

The Man exits and Mrs Walker enters carrying shopping

Mrs Walker Morning, Mr Perks.
Perks Morning, Mrs Walker. Been doing your shopping?
Mrs Walker Busy day today.
Perks Busy day today.
Mrs Walker How's the family, Mr Perks?
Perks Very well.
Mrs Walker Good.
Perks In fact the kids are playing around here somewhere. The missus went into town and lumbered me with the little devils. I've never known kids get up to so much mischief.

Six little faces appear—John, Alfred, Edith, Bert, Emma and Joan—on different parts of the stage

Mrs Walker Oh they're all right, Mr Perks, you're very lucky.
Perks Oh ay.
Mrs Walker Kids are only kids, aren't they?
Perks Yeah, well any time you fancy taking a couple off me hands, you're welcome.
Mrs Walker (*laughing; moving off*) Right, I'll remember that.

As Mrs Walker moves off a leg pops out and half trips her up. Perks sees it

Perks John!
Mrs Walker (*with forced lightness*) No harm done.

Mrs Walker exits

John Hello Dad.
Perks Don't "hello Dad" me, where are the rest o' the tribe?

John Dunno.

Perks I warned you this morning when you came out wi' me—no bother.

John No, Dad.

Perks And don't "no Dad" me.

John Yes, Dad. (*He sees the Railway Children who have been watching this, fascinated*) Who are them?

Perks (*turning*) Oh hello. If you've come for the Manchester train you've just missed it. Sorry.

Roberta We haven't come for any train.

John What have you come for then?

Peter We've come to look at the station, that's all.

Perks I haven't seen you three round here afore.

Roberta We only arrived last night. We're staying at the Three Chimneys Cottage.

Perks Oh so you're the ones. Mrs Viney were telling me all about you. Where are you from?

Phyllis We're from London.

John Oh so that's why you don't talk proper. (*He laughs*)

Perks He's pulling your legs, take no notice of him.

Phyllis (*indignantly*) And anyway we do talk *properly*.

John Oh la di da, listen to her.

Perks Now give over, John, and just show some respect. (*Seeing the other children*) Eh up, look what the dog's brought in.

Peter What dog?

Perks You what, son?

Peter Where's the dog? You said, "Look what the dog's brought in."

Roberta It's an expression, Peter. He doesn't mean, "Look what the dog's brought in", he means ... (*confused*) ... "look what ..." well, anyway, it's an expression.

Peter How stupid.

Perks (*to his children*) Come on, you lot, over here. I'd like you to meet some new friends. (*To the Railway Children*) What are your names?

Peter I'm Peter.

Phyllis I'm Phyllis.

Roberta I'm Roberta, though everyone calls me Bobby.

Alfred That's a boy's name.

Peter No, it isn't.

Alfred I've a friend called Bobby and he's a lad.

Perks It can be either, now stop arguing, you've only just met.

Alfred Well it is a boy's name!

Perks Will you stop arguing, and introduce yourselves to Peter, Phyllis and Roberta. You've met John already, he's me eldest.

John Hiya.

The Railway Children Hello.

Alfred I'm Alfred.

The Railway Children Hello.

Edith I'm Edith.

The Railway Children Hello.

Bert I'm Bert.
The Railway Children Hello, Bert.
Emma I'm Emma ...
Joan ... and I'm Joan.

Emma and Joan are holding hands as they do throughout the play

The Railway Children Hello.
Perks Good. And I'm Perks. Now, how long will you be staying at Three Chimneys?
Roberta We don't know.
Phyllis Until Father comes home.
Perks Oh ay? And where is your father?
Roberta He's working away.
Peter He has a very important job with the Government.
Perks Does he now. And what sort o' job's that?
Roberta It's very secret.
Bert (*all innocent*) Is he Prime Minister?
Roberta No.
Phyllis But it's very important because he can't talk about it.
Perks Then it must be important.
Peter It is.
Perks Anyroad ... *I've* an important job to do around here an' all and the Station Master'll be on me back unless I get on with it. (*To his children*) And remember what I said. No mischief.
Perks' Children Yes, Dad.

Perks goes

Alfred goes up to Peter and kneels behind him. John goes to Peter

John Hey, look up there.

All look up. John pushes Peter over Alfred's back. All laugh

Roberta Stop that!
John It's only a bit of fun.
Roberta It isn't at all funny.
Phyllis No, it's horrid.
John Only a joke.
Peter (*getting up*) It's all right, Roberta, I'm not hurt.
Roberta You could've injured his back.
John I've said I'm sorry, haven't I? You're worse than me mam.
Roberta You should have more sense at your age.
John Give over will you.
Bert Eh, dun't she talk funny.
Phyllis No we don't. You do.
Alfred We all talk like this round here.
Emma So you're the one who talks funny.
Joan Yes, you're the one who talks funny.
Emma So there.

Joan So there.
John There's only Miss Johnson who talks like you round here.
Roberta Who's Miss Johnson?
Bert She's our teacher.
Roberta Do you all have the same teacher?
Emma Yes.
Joan Yes.
Phyllis And do you only have one teacher?
Edith Course we do.
Peter Are you all in the same class then?
Alfred Yeh.
Peter Oh, that must be jolly good fun.
Edith We do reading, writing and 'rithmetic.
Alfred 'Cept she can't read yet.
Edith Yes, I can, I can read better than you.
Alfred No, you can't
Edith Yes, I can.
Alfred Can you heck.
Edith I can so there. (*To Phyllis*) Can you read?
Phyllis Yes.
Edith Big words?
Phyllis Oh quite big words, yes.
Edith I can only read little words.
Alfred Like cat and mat and sat.
Edith Oh shut up you, you don't know what you're talking about.
Phyllis That's not very ladylike, is it?
Edith Yer what?
Phyllis Talking to someone like that.
Edith Oh yeah, and what should I say?
Phyllis You should say, "Excuse me but I don't think you're quite right in what you're saying".
Edith Oh yeah? (*To Alfred*) "Excuse me but I don't think you're quite right in what you're saying." So keep your big fat mouth shut!

Everyone laughs

Bert I can write my own name.
Roberta Can you?
Bert Yeah.
Emma So can I and I'm only eight.
Joan So can I and I'm only ...

Joan forgets and Emma whispers in her ear

Seven.
Roberta (*to John*) How old are you?
John (*proudly*) Fourteen. What about you?
Roberta Fifteen.
John (*deflated*) Are you?
Roberta Do you go to school as well?

John (*proudly*) I leave next month.
Roberta Really? And what are you going to do?
John Work on the railways with me dad.
Peter How spiffing!
Alfred Spiffing?! What's spiffing?
Peter Something that's very good, stupid.
Roberta Don't be rude, Peter.
Alfred Yeah, or I'll give you a spiffing hiding.

They all laugh. Even Peter is amused

John I'm going to be an engine driver.
Peter (*impressed*) Are you really?
Alfred He doesn't know what he's going to be yet.
John Oh yes I do.
Peter I'd like to be an engine driver when I grow up.
John How old are you?
Peter Twelve.
Alfred I'm twelve an' all.
Bert I'm nine and two months.
John Are you rich?
Roberta Pardon?
John You talk all posh and that, you must be rich.
Roberta We used to be rich, but Mummy says we're poor now.
Alfred Mummy!
Phyllis She said we have to watch all our pennies.
John You don't look poor. Why are you poor?
Roberta You see while Father's working away he can't afford to send us
    any money.
John Why not?
Roberta He just can't.
John Where is he?
Roberta We told you, he's working away.
John Where though?
Roberta A long way away.
John How long's he going to be away?
Roberta Mummy doesn't know. She says it could be some time. You see it's
    all very secret because it's the Government.
Edith Will you be coming to our school on Monday then?
Phyllis Oh no, Mummy says we don't have to go to school. She's going to
    teach us.
Alfred No school?
Peter No.
Alfred I wish our dad'd go away so we could miss school!
Roberta No you don't.
Alfred I do. I hate school.
Bert I hate school an' all. It's horrible.
Roberta You should think yourselves very lucky you have your daddy at
    home with you. We wish we had, don't we?

Peter ⎫
Phyllis ⎰ (*together*) Yes, we do.

Alfred Well I still hate school.

Edith I'd like school if there weren't any teachers.

Alfred Yeah, so would I.

John Don't talk daft. If there weren't no teachers there wouldn't be no school.

Alfred Exactly!

Peter (*suddenly*) Listen!

The sound of an approaching train is heard

John It's the ten fifteen to London.

Roberta London!

Phyllis That's where Daddy is.

Peter Maybe we should wave to everyone on the train and imagine that we're waving to Daddy.

John Don't be daft.

Roberta I think it's a very good idea.

John It's soppy. Are you three simple or summat?

Roberta And don't be rude, John.

John tuts. The children congregate around the double doors leading to the platform

Peter (*leaning forward*) Here it comes through the tunnel.

Perks is seen on the platform

Perks All aboard for the ten fifteen express to London.

Much steam etc. Doors open and slam closed

Passengers come and go

Perks blows his whistle and then comes through the double doors

Roberta Come on . . . wave.

The children lean forward to wave. Peter, Phyllis and Roberta that is, plus Emma and Joan. The other children remain disdainful

Did you see that old gentleman in the first class compartment? He waved to us. Do you know him, Mr Perks?

Perks (*indicating his chest*) I know him from here upwards. But I couldn't even tell you if he's got a pair o' legs. He travels every day on the London express.

Roberta Does he always wave?

Perks Never seen him wave in me life afore.

Roberta Oh. Perhaps he likes us.

Perks Ay, perhaps he does. (*To his children*) Anyroad, you kids, I want you back in the house in ten minutes.

John Aw, Dad.

Perks And don't aw Dad me. Your mam's due back from town in a quarter of an hour.
Roberta We'd better go home as well.
Perks I expect I'll be seeing a fair bit o' you three then, will I?
Roberta That's if you don't mind our coming to visit the station.
Perks Not at all. You're welcome any time.
Peter Oh whizzo!
Alfred Whizzo?
John (*to Roberta*) We'll see you then.
Roberta Yes. Very nice meeting you, John.
John Yeah. Tara then.
Peter Tara?
Alfred Yeah, tara.
Peter Oh ... tara. (*And he smiles*)

All say "tara" to one another

   Perks' children exit

Perks After that they used to come to the station every day, ten fifteen sharp. Each morning they'd stand on the platform 'ere and wave to the old gentleman.

Roberta, Peter and Phyllis wave as Perks speaks

Children Send our love to Father.
Perks And each day the old gentleman'd wave back to 'em as regular as clockwork.

   The children exit

Perks moves the points and the set changes to the cottage

   Their mam used to write you know. Short stories. And she tried to sell 'em. Now I'm all right at telling stories but not much use at writing 'em.

Mother is working at a laid table. The children join her and she sets aside her papers

   Anyroad, she were that busy the three kids only seemed to see her at meal times. And for the first time in their lives they knew the meaning o' poverty.
Mother Phyllis, darling, jam or butter, not jam and butter.
Phyllis Oh, Mother.
Mother We can't afford that sort of luxury nowadays, darling.
Perks And when they hadn't enough food their mam'd say ...
Mother I'm not very hungry today, my lovelies, you eat the rest of this.
Perks But now and again their mam'd announce ...
Mother I've sold a story, my darlings.
Peter Oh smashing!
Phyllis That's terrific, Mother.
Perks And they'd all have buns for tea. They loved that. But most times

they were like me; couldn't afford nothing fancy. Course, the way their mam neglected herself it weren't long afore she fell ill, poor thing ...

Mother leaves the table and mounts the stairs to her bed

She were so bad one morning she hadn't even the strength to get out o' bed.

Peter and Phyllis exit

Roberta moves up to join her

Roberta Oh Mother, how are you?
Mother I don't know what all the fuss is about. I only have a headache, that's all, and a little sore throat.
Roberta Your face is very red.
Mother That's because it's so warm in here.

Roberta touches her Mother

Roberta Mother, it's freezing cold in here, but you're burning.
Mother I'm perfectly well. A day in bed and I'll be fine.
Roberta The doctor will be here in a minute.
Mother I don't know why you wanted to call the doctor in the first place. We shouldn't be bothering him, I'm sure he's busy enough as it is. And anyway we really can't afford a doctor.
Roberta Would you like a cup of tea, Mother?
Mother It's very kind of you, Bobby, but I don't want you fussing. I'm perfectly well enough to make my own tea. (*She tries to get out of bed but fails*)
Roberta Mother, are you all right?
Mother A little dizzy, that's all.

The Doctor enters downstairs with Peter and Phyllis, and goes up to Mother's room

Doctor Now then, what have we here? Good-morning. I'm Doctor Forrest.
Mother (*shaking hands*) Very pleased to meet you. I'm terribly sorry to bring you out.
Doctor Not at all. How are you?
Mother I don't want to be any trouble to you, Doctor.
Doctor And you won't be. (*To the children*) Anyway, I'd like you all to leave the room while I examine your mother. I won't be long.

The children leave the cottage to play in the garden

Perks Dr Forrest spent about ten minutes examining their mam and when he came out he wanted to speak to Roberta.

The Doctor enters the garden

Roberta How is she?
Doctor She's going to be fine.
Roberta She isn't *very* ill, is she?
Doctor Not at all. She has influenza.

Roberta Is that serious?

Doctor Not if we all look after her. Now, what's your name, young lady?

Roberta Roberta.

Doctor Well Roberta, I expect you'll want to be head nurse.

Roberta Oh yes.

Doctor Then I'll send down some medicine. Light up a fire in the room. Have some strong beef tea made ready to give her as soon as the fever goes down. She can have grapes now, and beef essence—and soda water and milk, and you'd better get a bottle of brandy. The best brandy. Cheap brandy is worse than poison. There are one or two other things and I've written them all down for you. (*He hands Roberta a list*)

Roberta Thank you. Only . . .

Doctor Yes? (*A pause*) Only what? Out with it.

Roberta It's rather hard you see—to . . . out with it. Because—because of what Mother said.

Doctor What *did* she say?

Roberta She said I wasn't to go telling everyone that we're poor. But you aren't everyone, are you?

Doctor Not at all. So?

Roberta Well . . . I know doctors are very extravagant . . . I mean expensive, and Mrs Viney told me that her doctoring only cost her twopence a week because she belonged to a club . . .

Doctor Ah . . .

Roberta You see she told me what a good doctor you were and I asked her how she could afford you and then she told me about the club and I thought I'd ask you and . . . oh Doctor, I don't want Mother to be worried. Can't we join the club too, the same as Mrs Viney.

A pause. The Doctor smiles and sighs

You aren't cross with me are you?

Doctor Cross? How could I be? You're a very sensible lady. And you mustn't worry. I'll make sure everything is fine with your mother even if I have to make a special brand new club.

Roberta Oh thank you, Doctor.

Doctor So stop worrying. And that's doctor's orders. Now take that list up to your mother and I'll come and visit her again very soon.

Roberta Thank you very, very much, Doctor.

The Doctor exits

Roberta goes into Mother's room

Mother, the doctor's given me this list.

Mother takes it, looks at it and gives a little laugh

Mother I can't afford all this rubbish, my lovely. Tell Mrs Viney to boil two pounds of scrag end of neck for your dinner tomorrow and I can have some of the broth. There's a shilling on the sideboard to buy it. I should like a glass of water now and then I'll be perfectly happy. All right?

Roberta Yes, Mother.

Roberta leaves Mother's room and joins Phyllis and Peter in the garden

We've got to do something. Mother won't get well if we can't buy all the things on this list.

Phyllis But we haven't got any money.

Roberta She's given me a shilling to buy some scrag end of neck for our tea but she's just going to have the broth.

Peter We can do without the beastly mutton. Bread and butter will support life. People have lived on less on desert islands many a time.

Phyllis But even if we don't have anything to eat at all we still won't have enough money to get all those things.

Roberta No. We must think of some other way.

Perks And that's what they did. They thought harder than they'd ever thought before. And after a long long time they came up with an idea.

Peter and Phyllis exit and then enter with a large white sheet

Roberta Now take that down to the tunnel, hold it up high so the old gentleman can see, and I'll wait at the station. You understand that?

Phyllis Yes.

Roberta Peter?

Peter Of course I understand.

Roberta Go on then. Hurry. We haven't much time.

Peter, Roberta and Phyllis exit

Perks And at ten fifteen Peter and Phyllis held high their white sheet with the message, just as the train passed by.

Perks moves the points and the set changes to the tunnel

Peter and Phyllis enter and stand at the front of the tunnel. On their sheet are written the words "LOOK OUT AT THE STATION"

The train passes. Perks moves the points and the set changes to the station

Peter and Phyllis exit

And Roberta rushed down to the station and got there as the train arrived.

Roberta enters the station, a note in her hand

A train pulls in behind the station double doors. Much steam etc.

Roberta rushes on to the platform. Perks follows

Roberta (*off*) Sir ... sir ... please take this note and read it. Please sir, we need help.

Perks (*off*) Be careful, girl, that's dangerous.

John, Alfred and Edith enter. Perks brings Roberta in, back off the platform

(*To Roberta*) I don't know what you were doing, young girl, but you could've got yourself killed.

Roberta I'm sorry, Mr Perks.

Perks Just you remember in future. (*He turns to leave, then pauses to speak to his children*) You're not up to no mischief, are you?
All No, Dad.
Perks That's all right.

Perks exits

John What were you doin' anyroad?
Roberta Oh hello.
Alfred What were you givin' that old gentleman?
Roberta Just a note.
Edith What for?
Roberta To help Mother.
John How is she now?
Roberta She's still not well. You see the doctor's given us this list of things Mother needs but we just can't afford to buy them.
Edith What's that to do with the old gentleman?
Roberta We were—we were asking him for help.
John You mean scrounging?
Roberta Sorry. I don't understand.
John That's scrounging.
Roberta What d'you mean?
Alfred It's like begging.
Roberta It never is!
Edith I'd scrounge if my mam were ill.
Roberta Of course you would—and anyway—it isn't . . . scrounging as you call it.
John I call it scrounging.
Roberta You would.
John You don't even know him.
Roberta Yes we do!
John Have you ever spoken to him?
Roberta Not exactly—but we've waved.
Alfred What's his name?
Roberta The old gentleman.
John Is that his first name or his second?

John and Alfred laugh

Roberta Anyway, I don't care what you think—I'd do anything to make sure Mother gets well again—so there. (*And she turns on her heels and moves off*)
John (*after her*) We didn't mean it.

Roberta turns. John goes up to her so that they are on their own

We didn't. It's just—it's just that . . . well . . . you're a bit stuck up sometimes, aren't you?
Roberta I beg your pardon?
John You're a snob.
Roberta Oh no I'm not!

John Yes, y'are. You think you're too good for us, don't you?
Roberta No, I don't.
John You do.
Roberta Honestly I don't, I don't really.
John You're not like us though, are you?
Roberta I've never thought about it.
John Well you're not. Is your mam going to be all right?
Roberta Yes—if we get all these things she needs.
John Can we help?
Roberta I don't think so—but thank you. (*She is about to go, but turns*)
John—would you say you're poor?
John We're not rich.
Roberta But are you poor?
John No. Course we're not. Me dad'd go spare if he heard you say that.
Roberta Why?
John He just would.
Roberta Have you got a big house?
John It's the station house. It's big enough. Three bedrooms.
Roberta Three? For eight of you?
John That's big enough. Mam and Dad have their room with the baby.
Edith, Emma and Joan share a bed in theirs, and me and me brothers
have a bed in ours.
Roberta You all sleep together?
John Yeh. What's wrong wi' that?
Roberta It can't be very comfortable.
John It's OK—so long as you all turn over at the same time.

They all laugh

Anyroad ... best be going. Tara then.
Roberta Yes ... (*She hesitates but smiles*) Tara.

All the children exit

A train is heard

Perks enters and changes the points

The set changes to the cottage

Perks (*collecting a hamper*) That evening a big great hamper was delivered
to the station, with a note to take it to the children at Three Chimneys
Cottage. And that's what I did. (*He moves towards the cottage*)

Roberta, Peter and Phyllis are downstairs

Peter It's Mr Perks! With a large hamper!
Roberta It must be from the old gentleman.
Perks (*struggling breathlessly*) Oh my God! The hills don't get no smaller.
This here's from the old gentleman. (*He drops the hamper on his foot and
cries out*)
Roberta Thank you very much, Mr Perks. This is wonderful.

Perks I don't know about wonderful. It were blinking heavy!

Peter Thank you anyway.

Perks S'all right. Anyroad ... hmm ... (*Blowing*) I'm out o' puff ... now ... Hmm.

Peter (*quickly*) Oh I'm awfully sorry, I haven't got twopence to give you like Father does, but ...

Perks I beg your pardon, young lad?

Peter Well Father always tips twopence to——

Perks I don't want none o' your twopence. I were just about to ask how your mother is, that's all.

Peter Oh, I'm awfully sorry.

Perks And I've fetched her along a bit o' sweetbriar, that's what I were going to say.

Roberta Oh we're terribly sorry, I hope Peter didn't offend you.

Perks Anyroad, here y'are. (*And he produces a bunch of sweetbriar from his hat*)

Roberta It's very kind of you.

Perks That's all right.

Peter And I really do beg your pardon about the twopence, Mr Perks.

Perks We'll just forget it, eh?

Peter Yes.

Perks And I'll wish you a good-night and hope your mother's better soon.

The children bid him good-night

Perks exits

Peter Come on then, let's get it open.

Excitedly the children open the hamper

Roberta Oh there's more here than we asked for.

Phyllis Peaches!

Roberta Port wine!

Peter I'll have some of that.

Roberta No you certainly won't!

Phyllis A chicken!

Roberta Oh and look at these roses.

Phyllis What a kind gentleman he is.

Peter Here's a letter!

Roberta Oh. Read it out.

Peter (*reading*) "Dear Roberta, Phyllis and Peter. Here are the things you want. Your mother will want to know where they came from. Tell her they were sent by a friend who heard she was ill. When she is well again you must tell her all about it, of course. And if she says you ought not to have asked for the things, tell her that I say you were quite right, and that I hope she will forgive me for taking the liberty of allowing myself a great pleasure." It's signed GP. I can't read that properly.

Phyllis Well I think we were right.

Roberta Right? Of course we were right.

Peter All the same I don't exactly look forward to telling Mother the whole truth about it.

Roberta We're not to do it till she's well and when she's well we'll be so happy we shan't mind a little fuss like that. Now—take the roses up to her.

Phyllis And the sweetbriar!

Roberta Oh yes, you musn't forget the sweetbriar!

Peter and Phyllis exit with the flowers. Perks enters and moves the points

The set changes to the tunnel

Perks And within two weeks their mam was much better. So they got out another banner and when the ten fifteen came out of the tunnel Phyllis and Peter were there to greet it.

Peter and Phyllis enter and stand before the tunnel. They have a sheet with the words: "SHE IS NEARLY WELL THANK YOU"

The train passes

Peter and Phyllis exit

But the fireworks were yet to come. When their mam was nearly better they had to tell her what they'd done. Well, it was a right little set to I can tell you. (*He changes the points*)

The set moves back to the cottage

Mother, Roberta, Peter and Phyllis are in the cottage

Mother Children, how could you do such a thing!

Phyllis We were thinking of you, Mummy.

Mother A complete stranger!

Roberta We were worried about you.

Peter Yes and so was I.

Mother That is not the point. I feel ashamed.

Roberta Why, Mummy?

Mother Absolutely ashamed. Who is this—this old gentleman?

Phyllis He's an old gentleman who travels every day on the ten fifteen.

Mother But who is he?

Roberta I don't know.

Mother You don't know?

Roberta Oh Mummy——

Mother You've never spoken to him?

Phyllis We waved to him.

Mother What must he think of me—letting my children beg for me.

Roberta It wasn't begging, Mummy.

Mother That's exactly what it was.

Phyllis Oh Mummy, please don't get angry.

Roberta We were only doing what we thought was best.

Peter We're sorry Mummy.

Phyllis
Roberta } (*together*) Yes, we're sorry.

All three burst into tears. Mother puts her arm round them

Mother All right, my lovelies, calm down. I'm sorry I was so angry because I know you don't understand.
Roberta We didn't mean to do wrong, Mummy.
Mother I know you didn't. But listen to me. It's quite true that we're poor, but we do have enough to live on. You mustn't go telling everyone about our affairs—it's not right. And you must never, never ask strangers to give you things. Now always remember that, won't you?
All Yes, we will.
Mother And I'll write a letter to your old gentleman and I shall tell him that I didn't approve—oh, of course I shall thank him too for his kindness. It's you I don't approve of, my darlings, not the old gentleman. He was as kind as ever he could be. And you can give the letter to Mr Perks to give to him—and we won't say any more about it.

Perks moves the points and the set changes to the station. A train is heard

Mother, Peter, Phyllis and Roberta exit

Perks So that's what she did and after the old gentleman seemed to wave even more than before.

Peter, Phyllis and Roberta enter the station with the Perks' children

Peter }
Phyllis } (*together*) Send our love to Father.
Perks And he'd smile at 'em and they right wanted to speak to him but they never would. Course they started spending more and more time hanging round here. Not that I minded of course, so long as they didn't stop me working.

Peter, Roberta, Phyllis and the Perks' children are now sitting around the station. Perks goes to join them

Peter What are those things that hook the carriages together?
Perks Those "things" as you call 'em, are called couplings.
Peter And those pipes that hang over the couplings, what are they for?
John They help stop the train.
Perks Our John here knows almost as much about railways as I do. Don't you, lad?
John (*beaming*) The other way to stop the train is to pull the communication cord.
Phyllis What's a ... (*she has difficulty saying it*) ... communication cord?
Perks It's that thing in the carriage which says, "Five pounds fine for improper use". If you were to improperly use it the train'd stop.
Roberta And what if you used it properly?
Perks The train'd stop just the same. But anyroad, it isn't proper use unless you're being murdered.
Phyllis }
Peter } (*together*) Murdered!
Perks Or summat nearly as bad as that.
Peter Are all engines the same?

Perks Good lord no! No more than me and you are. Take that little 'un what went by ten minutes ago, the one without a tender—that was a tank—she's off to do some shunting further down the track.
John Then there's goods engines.
Perks Great big things they are with three wheels each side. (*Suddenly*) Eh up, I can hear the eleven twenty. Right, you lot, if you'll excuse me, I've work to do.

Perks stands up and comes forward as we hear a train approaching the station. It stops and we hear the sound of carriage doors. Perks blows his whistle

This is the eleven twenty calling at all stations to York.

As he blows his whistle again and the train pulls out, there is a noise off stage

Eh up, what's going on here then?

A man, Mr Szczepansky, looking very confused and frightened, enters with two or three people surrounding him, jostling him slightly

Woman He wants putting away in one o' them hospitals.
Man 1 I'd say the police should deal with it.
Man 2 Look at his eyes. There's summat not right about him.
Woman He's certainly very peculiar.
Perks What's going on then?

The children all gather round

Woman He's just been put off the train for having no ticket.
Perks Has he now?
Man 1 What's more, he wouldn't go.
Perks Is that right? Where was he going to?
Man 2 That's the thing, he doesn't speak proper. Ask him summat.
Perks Where are you going?

Mr Szczepansky does not answer

Woman Look at him. See what I mean?
Roberta He's frightened, that's all.
Woman Frightened!
Roberta You can see it in his eyes.
Man 1 Ask him another question.
Perks Where are you going to?

Mr Szczepansky speaks in a foreign language: "I am lost—I am ill"

Woman You see what I mean?
Man 2 He's not from round here.
Perks Where are you from?

Mr Szczepansky speaks again. "I am lost. I am ill. Where am I?"

That's a funny old accent.
Bert Is he from London?
Perks They don't even talk that funny in London.

Man 1 Maybe he's French.
Peter No, it isn't French.
Woman What is it then, clever clogs?
Peter I don't know what it is but it isn't French. I know that.
Man 1 Try him with French if you know so much about it.
Peter All right—I will. Parlez-vous Français?

For a moment, Mr Szczepansky looks confused. Bert imitates Peter's accent

Bert Parlay voo frongsay?
Mr Szczepansky Je parle Français. Je suis malade. Aidez-moi je vous en
   prie. Je me perds. J'ai besoin de secours. Je suis sans ressource. Je ne
   comprend pas.
Peter There—now that's French. He can speak French but *he* isn't French.
Perks What does he say?
Peter Oh I don't know—he talks too quickly.
Perks (*to Mr Szczepansky*) Are you French?
Mr Szczepansky Je ne comprends pas, monsieur.
Roberta Mr Perks, why don't you take him aside—he's frightened by all
   these people.
Man 1 Why should he be frightened of us if he's nowt to hide.
Woman Ay, that's what I say?
Roberta Look at him, Mr Perks. Mother's due here any minute, she's going
   into town—let's wait for her, she speaks very good French.
Man 2 I say, let's call the police.
Man 1 Yes, hand the fella over to the police.
John Why he's done nowt wrong.
Woman He's a madman if you ask me.

As the crowd presses forward Mr Szczepansky cowers

Roberta Mr Perks, please.
John Yeah, leave him be.
Perks All right you lot, get back.
Roberta I know a few French words, let me try to speak to him.
Perks Well I suppose it won't do no harm.
Roberta Thank you. (*She comes forward*) I'll try and tell him my mother
   speaks French and that he mustn't be afraid, because we're kind. (*A
   moment*) Vous attendre. Ma mère parlez Français. Nous ... What's the
   French word for being kind?

Everyone shrugs—"I don't know"—"Don't ask me" etc.

Phyllis "Bong" is good.
Roberta Nous être "bong" pour vous.

Suddenly Mr Szczepansky takes hold of Roberta's hand gratefully

Mr Szczepansky Merci, merci.
Roberta There. You see.

Mother enters

Peter Here's Mother now!
Phyllis Mummy!
Mother What is going on here?
Roberta Mother, you've got to help us with your French.
Mother Sorry, Bobby. (*Seeing Mr Szczepansky*) Ohh—who's this?
Perks That's what we'd all like to know, ma'am.
Roberta He's foreign, Mother.
Peter But he can talk French.
Roberta Though he isn't French and we can't understand him.
Perks What's more, he hasn't got a ticket.
Man 1 We think he's up to no good.
John He's only frightened, that's all.
Mother Well give me some room, I'll see what I can do.

They all move back

Où habitez-vous? A quel pays?
Mr Szczepansky Le Russe.
Mother Et qu'est ce que vous faîtes ici?
Mr Szczepansky J'ai abordé ce train en erreur et je fit perdre mon billet. Madame, je suis malade.
Perks Well, ma'am?
Mother He's Russian.
Children Russian?
Mother Yes.
Perks He's got on the wrong train then, hadn't he?

There is a general chorus of laughter

He should have changed at Crewe for Russia.

More laughter

Mother He says he's lost his ticket. He also says he's very ill, though I haven't been able to find out what's wrong with him.
Woman It's the plague!
Man 1 |
Man 2 | (*together*) The plague?

Mother I can assure you it's nothing of the kind. Mr Perks, if you don't mind, I'd like to take him home with me. He's really quite worn out and I'll send one of the children for Dr Forrest. Is that all right?
Perks Fine by me, ma'am. I wouldn't know what to do with him anyroad.
Mother Of course I'll let you know tomorrow how things are.
Perks Fine by me. (*To the others*) Come on now—circus is over for today— (*to his children*)—and that includes you lot.

Perks' children moan and finally exit

Mother Roberta, will you call on Dr Forrest?
Roberta Yes, Mother.
Mother And Phyl and Peter, you come back with me.
Phyllis |
Peter | (*together*) Yes, Mother.

All exit, except Perks

Perks Roberta rushed down to Dr Forrest's and almost out of breath, explained what had happened and said he was to come as quick as possible and when they arrived back at the cottage the Russian man was already in bed. What a palaver it all was.

Perks changes the points. The set changes to the cottage

Mr Szczepansky is now in bed. Mother, Phyllis, Peter and the Doctor are around it

Doctor The man seems worn out, mind and body.
Mother It's such a dreadful shame. What about his cough?
Doctor Oh that can be cured. He needs a long rest—and keep the fire lit at night in here. He seems to be very poorly clothed. Have you anything he could wear?
Mother I should be able to dig something up.
Doctor Good.
Mother And thank you for coming in such a hurry—we always seem to be calling on you.
Doctor Not at all.

The Doctor leaves

Mother goes to the trunk and takes out men's clothes. She lays them on the floor

Roberta enters with a tray, sees the clothes and puts down the tray

Roberta (*picking up the clothes*) Daddy's clothes! What are Daddy's clothes doing here? Why hasn't he taken them with him? (*She finds a nightshirt among the clothes*) Mother ...
Mother Darling?
Roberta Daddy isn't ... dead is he?
Mother My darling, no, of course he isn't. What makes you think that?

Mother sees Roberta is holding the nightshirt

Oh Bobbie—when you go away for a short time do you take all your clothes with you?
Roberta No, but ...
Mother No "buts". Daddy was quite quite well when I heard from him last and I'll promise he'll come back to us some day.
Roberta But when, Mummy?
Mother As soon as he can, darling. Now stop worrying. (*She turns to Mr Szczepansky in his bed and starts to talk French to him*) Êtes-vous à l'aise?
Mr Szczepansky Oui, merci.
Mother Avez-vous besoin de quelque chose?
Mr Szczepansky Rien, merci beaucoup. Je suis bon.

While Perks speaks, Mother and the children move to the table

Perks She's a right little worrier is Roberta. Anyroad it was after they'd had summat to eat that their mam told 'em all about the Russian.

Phyllis Make a nice long story of it, Mother.

Mother I can't make a long story of it tonight . . .

Phyllis Oh Mummy.

Mother Because I'm very tired.

Phyllis Well make it as long as you can.

They sit down and start to eat

Mother Well it's a story long enough to make a whole book. He's a writer, he's written wonderful books. In Russia, with the Tsar, one dare not say anything about the rich people doing wrong, or about the things that ought to be done to make poor people better and happier. If one did one would be sent to prison.

Peter But they can't. People only go to prison when they've done wrong.

Mother Or when judges think they've done wrong. That's so in England but in Russia it is different. And he wrote a beautiful book about poor people and how to help them. I've read it. There's nothing in it but good and kindness. And they sent him to prison for it. He was three years in a horrible dungeon with hardly any light, and all damp and dreadful. In prison all alone for three years.

Peter But, Mother, that can't be true now. It sounds like something out of a history book—the Inquisition or something.

Mother It *is* true. It's all horribly true. Well then they took him out of prison and sent him to Siberia, a convict chained to other convicts—wicked men who'd done all sorts of crimes—a long chain of them, and they walked, and walked, and walked, for days and weeks, till he thought they'd never stop walking. And overseers went behind them with whips——

Phyllis ⎫
Peter ⎭ (*together*) Whips!?

Mother Yes, whips to beat them if they got tired. And some of them went lame, and some fell down, and when they couldn't get up and go on, they beat them, and then left them to die. Oh, it's all too terrible.

Roberta Oh Mother.

Mother And at last he got to the mines, and he was condemned to stay there for life—for life, just for writing a good, noble, splendid book.

Phyllis Oh, that's awful, Mother!

Mother He was telling me how he believed that one day all the poor people would rise up against the rich and they would fight and fight until all men, all women and all children were equal.

Roberta Oh how wonderful!

Mother He says that many people are talking like this and one day it will happen and everyone will be free and everyone will be equal.

Phyllis Mummy . . .

Mother Yes, my darling?

Phyllis Were we once rich?

Mother Well—not rich—but very comfortable.

Phyllis But we weren't horrible like those rich people in Russia were we?

Mother Oh, I hope not, darling.

Roberta If I were rich again I would share out my money with all the people who were poorer than I—like Mr Perks and Mrs Perks and all their children.

Mother That's very noble of you, Bobby.

Peter How did he escape, Mummy?

Mother When the war came some of the Russian prisoners were allowed to volunteer as soldiers. And he volunteered. But he deserted at the first chance he got and——

Peter But that's very cowardly, isn't it? To desert? Especially when it's war.

Mother Do you think he owed anything to a country that had done *that* to him? He owed more to his wife and children. He didn't know what had become of them.

Roberta Oh he must have been so miserable.

Mother He was. For anything he knew they might have been sent to prison too. They do those things in Russia. But while he was in the mines some friends managed to get a message to him that his wife and children had escaped and come to England. So when he deserted he came here to look for them.

Peter Had he got their address?

Mother No, just England. He was going to London, but he got on the wrong train and lost his ticket and wallet.

Peter Oh do you think he'll find them—I mean his wife and children, not the ticket and wallet.

Mother (*emotionally*) I hope so. Oh I hope and pray that he'll find his wife and children again.

Phyllis Oh Mother, how very sorry you seem to be for him.

Mother Yes.

The Lights fade to a spot on Perks at the points. An engine is heard

Mother exits

Perks The Russian bloke was better the next day and the day after that better still, and on the third day he was well enough to go into the garden. The three children looked at him as if he'd just dropped out o' the sky. They wanted to be friendly to him. Then Phyllis had a good idea.

The Lights come up on Mr Szczepansky sitting in a chair in the garden. The children surround him—Peter and Phyllis give Mr Szczepansky some flowers. He smiles and nods

Phyllis Wouldn't it be absolutely lovely if we picked him wild strawberries?

Peter Oh rather. That's a spiffing idea.

Phyllis I think the ones we saw last week should be quite ripe by now.

Peter Phyllis—for a girl—you sometimes come up with some splendid ideas.

Phyllis Horrid boy!

Mother joins them in the garden. She carries a basket containing sandwiches

Mother (*handing Phyllis the basket*) Now you won't be too late, will you? I've made you a packed lunch seeing it's quite a good walk.
Phyllis Oh, thank you.
Mother Make sure you're back before dark.
Phyllis Yes, Mother.

The Lights fade to a spot on Perks who changes the points. The set changes to the tunnel aspect and the Lights come up on the children looking for strawberries

Roberta We must be there soon. We can't have missed them.
Peter I remember this part, I'm sure.
Phyllis I'm getting tired. Oh dear, my boot lace has come undone again.
Roberta It's getting quite late you know.
Phyllis (*doing up her lace*) Wait for me!
Peter I'm sure they were here somewhere.
Roberta I think a bit further on.
Phyllis We'll have to go back soon ... I'm ever so tired.
Roberta (*suddenly*) Hush ... what was that?
Peter Nothing.
Roberta I thought I heard a voice.
Peter Don't be silly ... out here?
Phyllis (*who has wandered off*) The strawberries are here. Oh and they are ripe. Look at them! (*She picks one and begins to eat it*)
Roberta These are supposed to be for our Russian gentleman.
Phyllis Oh he won't mind our having some—if he's such a gentleman.
Peter (*taking one*) Oh they are scrumptious!
John (*off*) Scrumptious!
Peter Who was that?
Roberta I told you I heard a voice.
Perks' children (*off*) We're coming to get you! We're coming to get you!

The voices off begin to moan

Phyllis (*frightened*) What is it? Bobby, what is it? I'm frightened.
Roberta All right, John—you can come out now. John.

All the Perks' children enter through the mouth of the tunnel, smirking

Phyllis Oh you horrid things, you really frightened me.
Peter They didn't frighten me.
Alfred Boo!

Peter jumps

Roberta How long have you been following us?
John Since the other side of the hill. What are you doing?
Phyllis Collecting strawberries for our Russian gentleman, and you can't have any so there.
Edith It was only a joke, Phyllis.
Phyllis A horrid joke.
Bert Anyroad, I don't like strawberries.

Emma I do.
Joan So do I.
John What have you got in there?
Roberta Sandwiches for a picnic.
John Oh great!
Phyllis They're not for you.
Roberta Phyllis.
Peter Phyl's quite right, they're not.
Roberta Are you hungry?
John Starving.
Roberta All of you?
Perks' children Yes.
John We've had nowt to eat since breakfast.
Peter Oh Bobby, there's not enough for all of them.
Phyllis There certainly isn't.
Roberta (*opening the basket*) Remember what the Russian gentleman said.
John What did he say?
Roberta That we should all be equal and we should share everything out fairly.
Alfred I'll go along wi' that—seeing as you've got the butties.
Peter What are butties?
Alfred Shall I show you?
Peter Please.

Alfred takes a small sandwich from the basket and swallows it

Alfred That were a butty. A cheese butty as a matter of fact—and very nice too.

They all laugh

Roberta Very well—you may all have a—a butty.

They all laugh and dig into the basket

Phyllis I don't think I like sharing—I'm still hungry.

Suddenly there is the sound of distant creaking

Roberta What's that? Hush?

The all listen. Bert sees it first, pointing

Bert It's that tree.
Peter Where?
Bert There. It's walking.
John Walking!
Alfred Don't talk daft, Bert.
Bert Look!

They stare at the tree, which is now shaking disconcertingly

Roberta The whole bank's caving in. Watch out! That tree's going to fall!

The tree falls across the front of the tunnel

Look at it!

John It's gone all over the line!

Bert Isn't that dangerous?

Peter 'Course it's dangerous, stupid.

Edith Don't call my brother stupid.

John Stop arguing, we haven't time.

Roberta Can we go back to the signal box and tell them?

John I don't know. What time is it?

Roberta By the dark it must be half-past six by now.

John It must. That means the six forty could be due past here any time now.

Alfred Unless it's already gone.

John It can't have done. No train's passed us in the last half hour, has it?

Roberta No.

Phyllis What are we going to do?

John I don't know, but we must be the only ones who know about it.

Peter Couldn't we pull it all off the line?

Alfred We'd never shift that lot, it's too heavy.

John Ssshhhush!

They all listen. In the distance a train is heard approaching

It's too late, it's here.

Children Oh no!

Roberta What are we going to do? We must do something! We must or there's going to be a terrible accident!

Bert (*looking in the tunnel*) I can see it coming!

There are lights from the tunnel as the train gets ever closer

Phyllis I'm frightened, what are we going to do?

Peter We can wave to it.

John They'll never see us in the dark.

Alfred Hurry up, it's getting closer!

John We need summat white to flag 'em down.

Edith I've got a hankie!

John They'll never see a hankie!

Peter What if we shout?

Alfred They'll never hear us.

Roberta I've got a white petticoat! We could use my white petticoat!

John Oh yeah, that's a great idea!

Alfred Come on then, hurry up!

Roberta Turn round, you musn't look.

The boys turn away

John Then hurry up!

Roberta I am doing.

Alfred Come on, Bobbie!

John Hurry up!

Roberta There. Turn round now.

The boys turn again

John Stand near the line! Hold it up!

Roberta holds it up and waves

Peter Don't stand *on* the line!
Phyllis Get back, Bobbie!
Roberta It's never going to see me!
John Wave it high!

The train is very close now, and very loud

Roberta It can't see me! It's never going to stop! (*She stands on the track*)
Peter Get back, Bobbie, you'll get killed!
Roberta It's not stopping! It won't stop!

All the children are shouting and waving. The train comes ever closer; wind in children's hair; lights in their faces; steam everywhere; the sound of squealing brakes. Finally the train rolls to a halt just in front of Roberta

Peter It's stopped . . . we've done it, we've done it!

Everyone cheers

John Are you all right, Bobbie?
Roberta I—I think so. Did it stop?
John Yes, it stopped!
Roberta Thank goodness for that.
John You were right brave, you were.
Roberta Oh dear, I don't think I feel very well. (*She faints*)

The train engine continues to idle as the Lights fade to——

—BLACK-OUT

ACT II

The Station

The whole cast are on stage for a presentation. The District Superintendent is in the middle of his speech. Standing apart from the crowd, looking on, is an old, distinguished gentleman

District Superintendent And so on behalf of the railway, on behalf of all the fortunate passengers whose lives were saved by the courageous deeds of these brave children, I would like to say thank you very, very much.

Applause

And as a token of our esteem and gratitude I would like to make a presentation to our brave young heroes. Roberta has already spoken to me and explained that in all there were nine children who were involved in saving the train—so if she and her brother and sister, Peter and Phyllis, could step forward, I will make the first presentation.

Roberta, Peter and Phyllis step forward. They are given a watch between them. They thank the District Superintendent. More clapping

And thank you. Now—John, Alfred and Edith—could you step forward please.

John, Alfred and Edith step forward, receive a watch and move back to their family

And finally, but not least—Bert, Emma and Joan ...

Bert, Emma and Joan step forward to receive a watch, then back to their family

And thank you all very much for coming.

Everyone claps and disperses except the Railway Children, the Old Gentleman and Perks who moves to the points

The children are looking at the watch. They in turn are scrutinized by the Old Gentleman. Perks goes to the points

Peter Isn't it splendid?
Roberta Terrific.
Phyllis (*listening to it*) It's going! Listen to it ticking.
Peter Who's going to keep it though, that's what I'd like to know.
Roberta We all have to share it.
Peter You mean break it into three?

Roberta No. Silly.

Peter I was only joking, Bobbie.

Roberta Today, Peter, you can have the watch, tommorrow, Phyllis, it's your turn, and the day after, mine and so on. What do you think?

Peter What an awfully good idea.

Phyllis Though I still think we should have had a watch each instead of all the Perks' children.

Roberta Phyllis, sometimes you are so selfish. That wouldn't have been fair at all, would it?

Phyllis Yes, it would.

Roberta Have you not listened to a word Mr Szczepansky has said?

Phyllis No I can't speak French or Russian.

Roberta You know very well what I mean.

Peter She does have a point, Bobbie. It was your petticoat—and you waved it.

Phyllis And you stood on the line and nearly killed yourself.

Roberta But they were there as well—they shouted and waved and screamed just as much as we all did.

Peter Yes, I suppose you're right—as usual.

Phyllis Oh Bobbie, sometimes you're too fair.

Peter has seen the Old Gentleman

Peter (*turning*) Who's that?

Roberta Where?

Peter Surely it can't be ...

Roberta Oh it is! It is!

Old Gentleman Good-afternoon, children.

Children Good-afternoon.

Roberta How very nice to meet you.

Old Gentleman And how very nice to meet you. At last.

All shake hands

Roberta I'm Roberta ...

Peter I'm Peter ...

Phyllis And I'm Phyllis ...

Roberta What are you doing here, sir?

Old Gentleman I came specially to meet you. I heard about the presentation and I wanted to come here personally and thank you.

Roberta Why?

Old Gentleman For helping to save my life.

Peter Save *your* life?

Old Gentleman Yes.

Roberta How?

Old Gentleman I was one of the passengers on the six forty train.

Roberta Oh, you weren't!

Old Gentleman Yes, I was.

Phyllis We didn't know.

Old Gentleman I was sitting at the very front of the train—if I hadn't been killed almost certainly I'd have been badly injured.

Roberta Oh, how terrible!

Old Gentleman Not so terrible. In the end it was quite an adventure.

Phyllis But you could've been killed!

Old Gentleman And so could many others—but thanks to you—and your friends—we weren't. So—thank you very much indeed. (*He formally shakes hands with them*)

Roberta Not at all.

Phyllis A pleasure.

Peter Absolutely!

Old Gentleman And if there's any other way I can help you or your mother I'll certainly try my best.

Roberta Really?

Old Gentleman Why—is there anything I can do?

Roberta Well you see—yes, there is something you may be able to help us with.

Old Gentleman If I can.

Roberta We have a Russian gentleman called Szczepansky staying with us at present. You see he's escaped from Russia because he was locked up in Siberia for writing a book all about poor people and he's come to England to find his wife and children because they're over here somewhere but he doesn't know where but he's ever so sad and lonely for them because he can't find them and we'd give anything if you would help to find them for us. Wouldn't we?

Children Yes.

Roberta Even our gold watch.

Peter (*unsure*) Ohhh.

Roberta We would.

Old Gentleman What did you say his name was—Fryingpansky?

Roberta Oh no. Szczepansky (*Spelling it*) S-Z-C-Z-E-P-A-N-S-K-Y I think, and you call it Shepansky.

Old Gentleman (*knowing the name*) Shepansky!

Roberta Do you know him?

Old Gentleman Bless my soul.

Roberta You do know him.

Old Gentleman I've read his book! It's translated into every European language. It's a fine book, a noble book. And your mother took him in?

Phyllis Yes.

Old Gentleman What a very good woman your mother must be.

Phyllis Of course she is.

Roberta And you're a very good man.

Old Gentleman And you are a little flatterer. (*Smiling*) Now—shall I tell you what I think of you?

Roberta Oh please don't.

Old Gentleman Why not?

Roberta I don't exactly know. Only—if it's horrid I don't want you to—and if it's nice I'd rather you didn't.

The Old Gentleman laughs

Old Gentleman Then I'll just say I'm very glad you asked me about this—very glad—and I shouldn't be surprised if I found something very soon. I know a great many Russians in London—and every Russian knows his name. Now tell me all about yourselves. We've got lots of time to talk before my train.

Perks is beside the points

Perks Well, like a right good gentleman he were true to his word and it were one sunny afternoon a few weeks later that he arrived back and went straight round to the cottage. (*He moves the points*)

The set changes to the cottage

The Old Gentleman and the children exit. Mother is in the garden hanging up washing

The clothes are those of her husband that Mr Szczepansky has been wearing. She hugs them to her chest

The Old Gentleman enters

Old Gentleman Good-afternoon.
Mother (*surprised*) Oh, good-afternoon.
Old Gentleman You must be the mother of Roberta, Phyllis and Peter.
Mother Yes. And er . . .
Old Gentleman I'm the gentleman your three lovely children wave to each morning.
Mother Oh, really—how very pleased I am to meet you. I've heard so much about you.
Old Gentleman And I of you.
Mother What a pleasant surprise. The children will be pleased.
Old Gentleman Actually I have called here for a very special reason.
Mother Oh?
Old Gentleman Did the children not tell you?

A moment, then it dawns

Mother Mr Szczepansky!
Old Gentleman Yes.
Mother (*excited*) You've found his wife and children?
Old Gentleman They're living in London.
Mother Oh how wonderful! We must tell Mr Szczepansky at once! And the children of course. (*Calling*) Bobbie. Phyl. Peter . . . ! Come here quickly! Bring Mr Szczepansky! Quickly! This is so exciting. I don't know how to thank you enough. (*Calling again*) Bobbie . . . Phyl!

Roberta, Phyllis and Peter enter

Roberta Mummy?

They see the Gentleman

Children Oh, hello.
Mother We have some wonderful news—go and get Mr Szczepansky, he's
reading in his bedroom.

Peter rushes off

Roberta You've found his wife and children?
Old Gentleman Yes.
Phyllis Oh how super!
Roberta And are they quite well?
Old Gentleman Yes, quite well.
Roberta Oh wonderful!
Old Gentleman I've told them where your Russian friend is staying and
they're so excited they can hardly wait to see him.
Mother Oh yes, I can imagine. We must pack his few things right away.
Phyl, go and pack Mr Szczepansky's items.

Phyllis goes

What time is the next train?
Old Gentleman Fifteen minutes. I'll telegraph to London so that his family
meet him at the station in London.
Mother Oh this is such wonderful news.

Mr Szczepansky enters looking very confused

Mr Szczepansky Hello. You see me?
Mother Monsieur Szczepansky, votre famille . . .
Mr Szczepansky Oui?
Mother Ils sont sain et sauf.
Mr Szczepansky Grâce à Dieu! Où sont-ils?
Mother À Londres.
Mr Szczepansky Londres? Oh merci—merci beaucoup! (*To the others*)
Merci, merci.
Roberta Tell him about his train, Mother.
Mother Mr Szczepansky, le train parti en quinze minutes.
Mr Szczepansky Oui—merci, merci. (*He shakes everyone's hand*)
Mother You must go, Mr Szczepansky. Go. Your train.
Mr Szczepansky Train—yes.
Mother Fifteen minutes. (*She holds up her fingers to indicate fifteen*)
Mr Szczepansky Fifteen?
Old Gentleman Are you ready? Êtes-vous prêt?
Mr Szczepansky Yes. (*Touching his clothes*) These. Yours.
Mother You keep them. (*Translating*) Pour vous.
Mr Szczepansky Merci. Thank you.
Old Gentleman Come on, Mr Szczepansky. (*Translating*) Vitement, Mon-
sieur Szczepansky—le train.
Roberta We'll see you again we hope.
Old Gentleman Yes, I hope so. Good-bye.
Mr Szczepansky Oui, bien sûr, merci.

The Old Gentleman and Mr Szczepansky exit amid a chorus of good-byes

Phyllis Oh isn't that exciting? He's going to meet his children after all this time.

Mother Yes, it's very exciting. (*She has calmed down, is reflective, almost sad*)

Phyllis The baby must have grown such a lot since he last saw her.

Mother Yes.

Phyllis I wonder whether Father will think I've grown. I have grown, haven't I, Mother?

Mother Oh yes. Yes, you have.

Peter And so have I, Mother. Haven't I?

Mother Yes, Peter.

Peter I hope Father still recognizes us when he comes home. He will, won't he Mother?

Mother (*with difficulty*) Yes. Yes, I'm sure he will.

Roberta (*sensing her Mother's reaction*) Come on, let's race down to the fence and wave to the train as it passes. Come on. I'll beat you both.

Peter Oh no you won't.

Peter, Phyllis and Roberta race off

Mother looks at her husband's washing on the line. She draws it close to her then breaks down

Roberta enters

Mother Oh, I thought you'd gone.

Roberta I let them run on.

Mother I hope they keep off the line.

Short pause

Roberta Are you all right, Mother?

Mother Yes, I'm quite well. Why?

Roberta I just wondered. (*She starts helping her mother hang up the rest of the washing*) Are you going to miss Mr Szczepansky?

Mother Yes. I expect I will—but I'm very happy for him.

Roberta Yes—so am I.

Another pause

Mother Bobbie, do you think Peter and Phyl are forgetting Father?

Roberta No, why?

Mother Today was the first time they've spoken about him for a long long time.

Roberta We often talk about him when we're by ourselves.

Mother But not to me. Why?

Roberta I ... you ... well ...

Mother Bobbie ...

Roberta Yes?

Mother Tell me. Why?

Roberta Well ... I thought you were so unhappy about Daddy not being here that I stopped talking about him.

Mother You're a lovely, thoughtful girl, Bobbie.
Roberta I hate to see you unhappy.

Mother squeezes Roberta

Mother Bobbie, darling—I'll tell you. Besides parting from Father, he and I have had a great sorrow—oh terrible—worse than anything you can think of. And at first it did hurt to hear you all talking of him as if everything were just the same. But it would be much more terrible if you were to forget him. That would be worse than anything.
Roberta Oh we would never forget him, Mother—never. Never ever.
Mother And you must keep thinking of him.
Roberta Oh I do—only . . .
Mother Yes?
Roberta The trouble—that you and he have had—it won't last always, will it?
Mother No. No, my dear, it won't.
Roberta And Father will return home, won't he, Mother?
Mother Yes, darling, he will.
Roberta I just wish—I wish I could comfort you more.
Mother Oh darling, you do! Do you think I haven't noticed how good you've all been, not quarrelling nearly as much as you used to—and all the little kind things you do for me—like cleaning and helping me in the kitchen and in the garden.
Roberta But that's nothing, Mother.
Mother It is to me. It's a great deal to me, darling. (*She hugs Roberta again*)
Roberta Oh I do love you, Mother.
Mother And I love you. *Very* much. (*Pulling away*) You won't say anything to the others, will you?
Roberta No.
Mother Good. And thank you for helping me with the washing.

Roberta and Mother exit

Perks So now she knew. Their mam was hiding some terrible secret from them. Course she didn't dare ask. She wanted to know . . . yet she didn't. And things might've stayed like that. 'Cept for one tiny twist o' fate. It all started down at the station.

Perks turns the points and the set changes to the station

Peter and Phyllis are sitting on a bench

It's a right pretty brooch you're wearing, Phyllis.
Phyllis Yes, it belonged to Mother. I always liked it and so she gave it me for my birthday.
Perks Oh have you had a birthday?
Phyllis Yes. When's your birthday, Mr Perks?
Perks My birthday? I gave up keeping birthdays afore you were born.
Phyllis But you must have been born sometime—even if it was twenty years ago—or thirty—or even fifty.

Perks Not quite as long as fifty, miss, if you don't mind. Tell you the truth,
I'll be thirty-five on the fifteenth of this month.
Peter Then why don't you keep it?
Perks 'Cos I've other things to keep than birthdays, that's why.
Phyllis Really? D'you mean secrets?
Perks No! The kids and the missus, that's what I mean.

John, Alfred and Edith enter. Roberta follows them in

And talk o' the devil. Now you three.
John Mam told us to get from under her feet.
Perks So she sent you down here to get under mine, did she?
Alfred We'll do no harm, Dad.
Perks That'll make a change.
Woman (*off*) Mr Perks—is the ticket office open?
Perks I'll be right with you. (*To the children*) If you must play anywhere go
and play on the railway line.

The children laugh

Perks exits

Peter But isn't that dangerous, playing on the railway line?
Edith He were only joking.
Alfred He always pulls our leg, our dad.
Phyllis Did you know it's his birthday next week?
John Is it?
Phyllis Didn't you know?
John He never keeps birthdays, Dad.
Edith Nor Mam.
Roberta Don't you ever buy him presents and things then?
John What with?
Alfred We can't afford it.
Roberta But everyone should celebrate their birthday. We always do.
John Me dad says when you get to his age there's nowt to celebrate.
Peter He's thirty-five you know.
Edith Is he that old?
Alfred He's ancient, in't he?
Phyllis No, he's not. You're only ancient if you're thirty-six years old.
John Anyroad, are you two ready?
Peter Where are you going?
Alfred Down the canal. Fancy comin'?
Peter Oh rather!
Alfred Does that mean yeah?
Roberta Not at the moment, thank you.
Peter I'll come.
Roberta No, you won't, Peter, I want to talk to you.
Peter Aw, Bobby—what about?
Roberta We'll follow you on in a few minutes.
John Right—see you then.

The Perks' children exit

Peter Why can't we go now?
Roberta I want to talk about Perks' birthday. I think we should do something special because he's been very good to us and everyone should celebrate their birthday.
Phyllis Hear, hear!
Peter Well, all right, but what do you suggest?
Roberta I don't know.
Phyllis We could make him a big card with "Happy Birthday" on it.
Roberta Yes, we could but it's got to be even more special than that.
Peter Oh I know!
Roberta What?
Peter Mr Perks is very popular, isn't he?
Roberta Yes, he is.
Peter Everyone in the village knows him and they all say hello to him.
Roberta Yes.
Peter So there must be lots of people in the village who'd want to give him things for his birthday.
Phyllis Oh yes!
Roberta I'm not so sure we should do that, Peter.
Peter Why not?
Roberta Remember what Mother said—we weren't to ask people for things.
Peter For ourselves she meant, not for other people.
Phyllis That's true.
Roberta I think we should at least ask Mother first.
Peter Oh what's the use of bothering Mother about every little thing. Especially when she's busy writing.
Phyllis I think it'd be lovely if all different people from the village gave Mr Perks a present.
Peter Yes, if I was Mr Perks I'd like to be given lots of presents.
Roberta I'm still not sure. What if Perks thinks it's charity like Mother did?
Peter Oh Bobby, it's different for birthdays. Presents aren't charity.
Roberta No, no, you're right, Peter . . .
Peter Terrific!
Roberta It isn't charity when it's your birthday. I think it's really a jolly good idea, Peter.
Peter Spiffing! I say, let's not bother with the canal, this is much more exciting.

Roberta, Peter and Phyllis exit

Perks enters

Perks Course, I knew nowt about any o' this. A blinking good job and all. The little beggars had been right through the whole village . . . Top to bottom. There was no-one they hadn't called on, nor no-one what hadn't coughed up summat. A tobacco pipe from the sweet shop, half a pound of tea from the grocers, a faded woollen scarf from the drapers—one what 'ad been in the window too long like—and a stuffed squirrel from the doctor, though what they thought I was going to do with that is anybody's guess. From their mam they'd got a bundle of old clothes, and she'd even baked a whole batch of cakes with me initials iced on the top. Anyroad they collected the whole lot together and on the day of me birthday up they trotted to the station carrying the gifts in a pram Mrs Ransome had given them.

Perks exits

Roberta, Phyllis and Peter enter, pushing a pram containing presents wrapped in newspaper. All the Perks' children enter and meet them

Roberta Where's your father?
John He's off down the line somewhere. What's that?
Roberta It's a surprise.
John Who for?
Peter Your father. They're presents we've collected for his birthday.
Alfred Collected?
Peter Yes.
John Who from?
Peter People in the village.
John What do you mean you went round asking for things for Dad?
Phyllis Yes, why?
John It is going to be a surprise for him. I think I'll keep out the road.
Alfred Good idea.
Roberta Why?
John You'll find out. (*To his brothers and sisters*) You lot had better come an all.

The Perks' children start to go

Roberta I'm sorry, I don't understand . . .
John You will.

Mrs Perks enters

Mrs Perks Where are you all going?
John Out.

Perks' children exit

Mrs Perks Oh. Oh hallo. What are you doing here?
Roberta We've brought Mr Perks some presents for his birthday.
Mrs Perks His birthday?
Phyllis Yes. He's thirty-five today.
Mrs Perks I know. He reminded me. I don't know what put it into his head to think of such a thing. We keep the children's birthdays o' course—but me and him—and you say you've brought him some presents?
Peter Yes. They're all in here.
Mrs Perks All these?
Peter Yes.

Mrs Perks Goodness gracious me! I don't believe it. Let me see. Really? All these for Perks?

Children Yes.

Mrs Perks Every one?

Children Yes.

Mrs Perks Well I can't believe it. I really can't. It's ... oh I think it's wonderful—it's wonderful ... all these just for Perks ... (*And she begins to sniffle*)

Roberta Oh, Mrs Perks!

Mrs Perks This is just too much.

Peter Too much presents?

Mrs Perks Oh it's wonderful, I think it's wonderful.

Peter Then I wish you wouldn't cry so.

Mrs Perks Wait till he sees all these presents. (*She blows her nose*) I'm sorry. It's just ... you will forgive me, won't you? I can't believe it. Perks has never had a birthday like this. Never. Never in his life. Even when he were a kid. I've been saving up just to buy him an ounce of his favourite tobacco, but now with all these presents ... What can I say? I don't know, I really don't know.

Roberta Don't say anything, Mrs Perks. We're glad you're pleased and we hope Mr Perks will be just as pleased.

Mrs Perks Pleased? Wait till you see his face!

Perks (*off*) And what are you lot doing round there?

Perks' children (*off*) Nothing, Dad.

Perks That'll make a change.

Perks' children (*off*) Happy birthday, Dad.

Perks (*off*) Oh, ta very much, ta very much indeed.

Mrs Perks He's here now.

Roberta Oh I think we should surprise him and hide.

Peter What a jolly good idea.

Phyllis Where can we hide, Mrs Perks?

Mrs Perks Er—in the office.

Roberta Right—you tell him about the presents—but give him the tobacco first and when you've told him we'll all come in and shout "Many Happy Returns."

Roberta, Peter and Phyllis exit

Perks enters

Perks Now then, lass.

Mrs Perks (*beaming*) Happy Birthday, Albert.

Perks Well what a birthday this is. First they remember—now you—eh up—what's this pram doing here?

Mrs Perks It's a present.

Perks A present? And what's all this lot in here? (*He picks up one of the presents which is wrapped in newspaper*)

Mrs Perks They're presents an' all, love. In't it wonderful?

Perks Who from? All the world and his wife? You didn't buy all these, did you, love?

Mrs Perks Oh no! I couldn't afford all these. This is my present. (*And she hands him a present*)

Perks Ta. So who are this lot from?

Mrs Perks The children, Albert.

Perks What children? Our children? How can they afford——?

Mrs Perks No! Them children from the Three Chimneys.

Perks What?

Mrs Perks Yes.

Perks All this lot?

Mrs Perks Isn't it wonderful?

Perks All this lot from them children. I can't take all this.

Mrs Perks Why not, Albert?

Perks Why not? You ask why not? Who do they think they are? Why their airs and graces, handing out charity——

Mrs Perks Shush, Albert!

Perks Handing out charity like they was lords and ladies——

Mrs Perks They're presents, not charity.

Perks Presents! One present, oh ay, but with all this lot it amounts to nowt more than charity! Well I'm not having it!

Mrs Perks Oh, Albert!

Perks I won't! I won't have it!

Mrs Perks Albert—can you be quiet. (*Mouthing*) They're in the ticket office listening.

Perks Oh are they? I'll give 'em summat to listen to. (*Calling*) Right you three—come out and tell us what you think you're up to. Come on.

Sheepishly, Roberta, Peter and Phyllis enter

Phyllis Oh Mr Perks, I though you'd be pleased.

Perks Pleased? When have I ever complained of being short of anything? Eh? Tell me that.

Roberta You've not, Mr Perks, but they're presents and people give presents on birthdays, what's wrong with that?

Perks Nowt's wrong with it. A present. One present—but when you've got heaps and heaps of 'em. Like this ...

Peter But they're not all from us.

Perks Oh no?

Roberta They're from all sorts of people in the village only we forgot to put labels on.

Perks People from the village?

Peter Yes.

Perks They've never given me presents afore so who put 'em up to it?

Phyllis (*all innocent*) Why, we did, of course.

Perks Well that is marvellous. That is blinking marvellous. So you've been round telling the neighbours we can't make both ends meet?

Mrs Perks I'm sure they didn't mean it, Albert.

Peter No, we didn't.

Perks Whether they meant it or not they did it. How can I hold me head up in the village now after this lot?

Phyllis I thought we were friends.
Perks So did I! I don't call this no friendship, showing me up like this.
Roberta Oh we didn't mean it, honestly we didn't.
Peter We didn't.
Phyllis Honestly.

The children start to cry

Mrs Perks Now look what you've done.
Perks Serves 'em right.
Mrs Perks I hope you're satisfied.
Roberta (*through her tears*) But you've got it all wrong, Mr Perks.
Perks Oh, have I indeed?
Roberta People gave you these presents not from charity but because they
    liked you.
Perks Oh yeah? I bet!
Roberta If you won't even listen!
Perks To what?
Mrs Perks You are stubborn old fool sometimes, Albert Perks. Why don't
    you listen for once in your life?
Perks Huh!
Roberta All I wanted to say was that—was that—well—everyone—who
    gave you a present passed on a message to you.
Perks Huh!
Mrs Perks Go on, love, he's listening.
Roberta These are clothes from Mother for your youngest. Mother said,
    "I'll find some of Phyllis' things that she's grown out of if you're quite
    sure Mr Perks wouldn't be offended and think it's meant for charity. I'd
    like to do some little thing for him because he's been so kind to you. I
    can't do much because we're poor ourselves."
Mrs Perks You see, Albert!
Perks Your mam's a born lady, I'll give her that. All right, we'll keep the
    clothes.
Roberta Then there's the perambulator and the gooseberries from Mrs
    Ransome. She said, "I dare say the Perks' children'd like these gooseber-
    ries." And she told me to tell you the pram was her little Emma's who
    died after six months and she'd like to see it used.
Mrs Perks Oh, I can't send the pram back, Albert.
Perks Am I asking you to?
Roberta Then the shovel. Mr James made it for you himself, and he said,
    "You tell Mr Perks it's a pleasure to make a little thing for a man what is
    much respected."
Perks I suppose James is a good enough fellah.
Roberta Then the honey and the bootlaces. Mr James said he respected a
    man who paid his way—and the butcher said the same. And the old
    turnpike woman said many was the time you'd lent her a hand with her
    garden when you were a lad—and things like that came home to roost—I
    don't know what she meant. And everybody who gave you anything said
    they liked you, and it was a very good idea of ours and nobody said

anything about charity or anything horrid like that and I thought you'd love to know how fond people are of you and I never was so unhappy in all my life. So good-bye. I hope you'll forgive us some day. (*Turning to the others*) Come on, let's go home.

Perks Now hold on a sec.

Mrs Perks I should think so too.

The children, still rather tearful, turn

Perks Maybe I've been a bit too hasty.

Mrs Perks A bit!!

Perks All right, lass. I'm sorry. And we will keep all the presents.

Children (*delighted*) Ohhhhhhhh!

Perks I can see you meant well—and to be honest—it's right grand to know you're well respected by your neighbours.

Peter Oh smashing!

Roberta Many happy returns, Mr Perks.

Perks Ta very much.

Phyllis Happy birthday, Mr Perks.

Perks Ta.

Mrs Perks And you will stay for tea now, won't you?

Roberta Oh yes, please!

Perks Right then, let's get those kids in an' we'll have a right good party.

Peter I'll go and get them.

Peter exits

Mrs Perks Well, what a fuss you've made over nothing, Albert.

Perks It's not nothing. If a man can't respect hisself then no-one else'll respect him neither.

Peter enters with all the Perks' children

Home-made decorations are taken from the pram and hung up. Perks opens his presents and the buns are handed round. Perks moves downstage

Eh and what a right lovely party we had. Lots of buns and tea and every one was jolly and happy and I've never seen Mrs Perks laugh so much in all her life. When we'd eaten all we could and drank so much tea the missus said it'd be coming out our ears, we realized how late it was, so Bobby, Phyl and Peter said they'd best be going.

Roberta Shall I take away all this wrapping for you, Mr Perks, and put it in the bin on the way out?

Mrs Perks That's very thoughtful of you, Bobbie. And I hope we'll see you again soon.

Roberta Oh yes, you will. Thank you for a lovely party.

Roberta picks up all the paper. She, Peter and Phyllis move off

(*To Phyllis and Peter*) I won't be a minute I'll just put these . . . (*She stops as she sees something on one of the papers. She reads it obviously shocked*)

Peter Come on, Bobbie, Mother will wonder where we are.

Phyllis Bobbie do hurry up.

The two children look at Roberta

Peter Bobbie . . .
Phyllis What's the matter, Bobbie?

They go up to Roberta and she hides the paper from them

Peter Are you all right?
Roberta (*almost inaudibly*) You go on—I'll catch you up.
Peter Why? What's wrong?
Roberta (*sharply snapping*) I said go on!

A moment; then Peter shrugs

Peter Come on, Phyl, I don't know what's wrong with her I'm sure. All that
tea's gone to her head.

Peter and Phyllis exit, puzzled

Roberta who is very shocked, reads the paper

Roberta (*to herself*) So now I know. (*Pause*) "End of trial. Verdict. Guilty.
Sentence. Five years penal servitude." Oh, Daddy—it's not true. I don't
believe it. You never did it. Never, never, never . . .

Everyone exits except for Perks

Perks So there we were. Well, what a palaver. That night her mam knew
there was summat up. (*He moves the points*)

The set changes to the cottage

Mother is sitting, knitting. Roberta enters from the garden

Mother Hello, darling.

Silence

Are Phyl and Peter in bed?
Roberta I suppose so.

Mother looks up and puts down her knitting

Mother Come and sit down, Bobbie.

Roberta sits. She still can't look up

You've been quiet all evening. Is there something wrong, darling?

*At first Roberta does not answer. Then she breaks down and rushes to her
mother*

Roberta Oh Mummy . . . oh Mummy!
Mother Darling—what is it? What's the matter?

Finally Roberta brings out the press cutting

Oh Bobbie . . . you don't believe it, you don't believe Daddy did it?
Roberta Oh no! No, of course not!

Mother Thank goodness for that! It isn't true. They've shut him up in prison but he's done nothing wrong. He's good and noble and honourable and he belongs to us. We have to think of that and be proud of him and wait.

Roberta Oh Daddy ... poor Daddy. (*And she clings to her mother again*) But why didn't you tell me, Mummy?

Mother Are you going to tell the others?

Roberta No.

Mother Why not?

Roberta Because ...

Mother Exactly. So you understand why I didn't tell you. We two must help each other to be brave.

Roberta Yes. (*Pause*) Mother—will it make you more unhappy if you tell me all about it?

Mother No. No, it won't.

Roberta I'd like to hear, Mother.

Mother Do you remember when we were living in London and two men arrived to see Father?

Roberta Is that when he went away?

Mother Yes. They were policemen. They took him down to the police station and charged him with selling state secrets to the Russians ...

Roberta But it can't be true!

Mother They called him a spy and a traitor.

Roberta As if Daddy would do such a thing. Russia! After everything Mr Szczepansky said about Russia—he wouldn't.

Mother Of course he wouldn't. But at his trial they brought up evidence that papers had been found in Father's desk.

Roberta What papers?

Mother Papers which proved he was guilty.

Roberta Then someone must have put them there.

Mother Exactly.

Roberta But who would do such a thing?

Mother Someone. And that someone is the guilty person.

Roberta But who could it be?

Mother I don't know. I don't know. The man under Daddy took Father's place when he—when the awful thing happened—he was always jealous of your father because Daddy was so clever and everyone thought such a lot of him. And Daddy never quite trusted that man.

Roberta Couldn't we explain all that to someone?

Mother Nobody will listen. Nobody at all. Don't you suppose I've not thought of everything. No—there's nothing to be done. All we can do— you and I and Daddy—is to be brave and patient and wait.

Roberta Oh Mother, you're so brave. Having to live with this and hide it from us. No wonder you looked unhappy sometimes.

Mother And darling—we won't talk of all this any more. We must bear it and be brave. And darling—try not to think of it. It's much easier for me if you can be just a little bit happy and enjoy things. Will you try?

Roberta I'll try, Mother, but it won't be easy.

The Lights fade to a spot on Perks who moves the points. The set changes to outside the tunnel. Mother exits

Perks And it wasn't neither. But she tried and she put on a brave face. And then she thought very hard about who could help her. Course, there was only one person. The Old Gentleman!

The Lights come up on Roberta sitting reading a letter she has just written

"My dear friend. You see what is in this paper. It is not true. Father never did it. Mother says someone put the papers in Father's desk and she says the man under him that got Father's place afterwards was jealous of Father and Father suspected him a long time. But nobody listens to a word she says but you are so kind and clever and you found out about our Russian friend's wife directly. Can't you find out who did the treason because it wasn't Father, upon my honour. Oh do please help me—there is just Mother and me who know and we can't do anything. Peter and Phyllis don't know. I'll pray for you twice every day as long as I live if you'll only try—just try to find out. Oh do, do help me. I remain your affectionate little friend, Roberta." (*She puts the letter in the envelope along with the newspaper cutting*)

John enters

John Hiya.
Roberta (*jumping*) Oh! You frightened me.
John What you doing?
Roberta Writing a letter.
John Who to, your dad?
Roberta (*flinching*) No. Our old gentleman.
John You're not begging off him again, are you?
Roberta Of course not. He's a very good friend. I often write to him.
John What about?
Roberta Anything. Are you going to the station?
John I might be.
Roberta Would you give this to your father and ask him to hand it to the old gentleman this evening when the train stops?
John OK.
Roberta Thank you. (*Short pause*) Would you miss your father if he were away?
John Dunno. Haven't really thought about it. Suppose so.
Roberta You don't know how lucky you are, John.
John No. (*And he looks at her and smiles sympathetically*) You're all right really, aren't you?
Roberta What d'you mean?
John You're not stuck up or owt, are you? Like I thought.
Roberta I hope not.
John I mean you do daft things but you can't help that.

Roberta smiles at John. There is a short pause. We hear Peter and Phyllis and the other children shouting off

Peter (*off*) Over here. Come on. There they go.
Alfred (*off*) There must be nearly twenty of 'em.

Peter, Phyllis and the five other Perks' children rush on

Phyllis Oh, 'ello you two.
John What's going on?
Peter It's a paper chase. The local grammar school.
John Oh, *them*. They're dead stuck up, they are.
Bert They won't even speak to us.
Roberta That's not very nice.
Edith No, it isn't.
Emma It isn't very nice at all. They're horrible.
Joan Horrible.
Peter (*looking off*) Here's the hare coming over the top of the hill now.

During the following the "Hare", Jim, enters and exits, followed by the "Hounds". The others begin to cheer

Phyllis The others won't be far behind him.
Edith What happens if they catch him?
Peter Oh I don't know.
Bert Well if he's a hare, maybe they'll eat him.
Alfred Don't talk daft, Bert.
Phyllis Oh I wouldn't like to eat him.
Peter Here are the hounds now.

They begin to shout—"Hey your shoelace is undone!"—"I could run faster wi' one leg!"—"Only another fifty mile!"—"Don't get lost!" etc.

Roberta That poor boy in the red jersey looks tired already.
John His face is redder than his jersey!
Alfred You'd be best catching the next train, lad!
Roberta Don't be cruel. The hare should be coming over the next hill ...
Peter Here he comes now!
John He's heading for the railway tunnel.
Roberta Isn't that rather dangerous?
Alfred Not if they keep to the side.
Phyllis There he goes!
Peter I say—let's go over the top and meet them at the other end of the tunnel.
Alfred (*taking the mickey*) I say—what a ripping idea!
Edith Come on then or we'll miss 'em.
Bert Eh, it's right exciting, in't it?

Perks changes the points and the set changes to the interior of the tunnel. The Lights dim. A train is heard approaching

Phyllis There's a train coming out of the tunnel.
Roberta Oh, I hope they're going to be all right.
John 'Course they are.
Peter Here's the hare now.
Alfred Beat you!
John Eh, you've dropped some paper!
Edith Keep running!
Bert They're catching up!

John They are an' all, here are the hounds!
Alfred That's it, then.
Peter No, it's not.
Alfred I can't see no-one else.
Peter Where's that boy in the red jersey?
Alfred Oh, yeah.
Bert I can't see him neither.
Roberta I wonder if he's all right?
Phyllis Maybe he's hurt.
Peter Maybe he's lying unconscious, his pale head resting on the rail.
Roberta Oh Peter, don't try and talk like a book.
John D'you think we should go in and have a look?
Edith I'm not going in.
Alfred Don't be soppy.
Edith I'm not.
Emma Nor am I.
Bert I'll go in. I'm not scared.
John You three'd best go home then. I think we should go and have a look for him.
Peter I think so too.
John Right—I'll go first. Follow me.
Alfred And you three go home.

John, Roberta, Peter, Phyllis and Alfred and Bert enter the tunnel

Edith Come on, you two.

Edith, Emma and Joan exit

In the tunnel voices echo and there is the sound of dripping water

Phyllis It's dark.
Bert It's right dark.
Alfred And it's damp.
Phyllis And cold.
John If you hear a train coming just press yourselves against the side, you'll be all right.
Phyllis I want to go back. I don't like it. It'll be pitch dark in a minute, I won't go on in the dark, I don't care what you say.
Peter Don't be a silly cuckoo. I've got a candle and matches in my bag.
Roberta It might be a good idea to light one, Peter.
Peter Very well. (*He takes a candle from his bag and lights it*) There, that's better.
Phyllis It still sounds funny.
John Be quiet a minute.

They all listen

Alfred It's a train.
John Get back off the line! Press yourselves against the wall. Quick!
Phyllis I'm frightened.

Peter Be quiet, Phyl.
Bert Eh, isn't this exciting?

The train rushes through the tunnel, blowing the candle out as it does so

Phyllis The candle's gone out!
John Is everyone OK?
Phyllis I'm frightened.
Roberta Light the candle again, Peter.
Peter (*as he does so*) I wish Phyl wouldn't be so soppy.
Phyllis Can we go back now?
Roberta No, we must find the boy. Hold my hand, Phyl.
Alfred What if the red jersey lad was lying on the line?
Phyllis Oh no!
Peter We must go and see. Come on.
John Stay close together.

Ahead they spot the boy, Jim

Alfred Look there!
Roberta It's him.
John Come on.
Phyllis Is he dead? Is that real blood?
Alfred Is it heck, it's only his jersey.
Phyllis But is he dead?
Roberta I think he's only fainted.
John Can we move him?
Roberta I don't know. He looks quite heavy.
Alfred Try and wake him.
Roberta But be careful.
Bert Put his head under one o' them drips, that'll wake him.
John Shut up, Bert!
Bert I were only saying.
Peter I've some milk in my bag.
Roberta Wet his ears with milk. I know they do it with eau-de-cologne to
 people who faint, but I expect milk's as good.
Phyllis He looks dead to me.
Peter Be quiet, Phyl. (*He pours the milk on Jim*)
Roberta Don't drown him.
Peter My hand slipped.

Jim groans

Roberta Oh thank goodness for that.
Phyllis He isn't dead.
Jim (*faintly*) Where am I?
Roberta What happened?
Jim Who are you?
Roberta I'm Bobbie. And these are friends of mine. We're in the railway
 tunnel.
Jim Oh I remember.

John Wha' happened then?
Jim I think—I think I tripped over a wire.
John Can you stand?
Jim I'll try. (*He does but winces and groans*) Oh I think I've broken my leg.
Roberta Oh dear!
Jim It's a terrible pain.
John Well we're going to have to get you out of here some way or other.
Alfred We'll have to carry him.
Jim How?
Alfred Well me and John are the biggest.
John Yeh, you're going to have to stand up you know.
Jim I'll try.
Roberta Do be careful.
John Put your arm round me neck and the other round Alfred's.

Jim does so but groans with pain

Phyllis Oh I do hate to hear that.
Bert His leg won't fall off if it's broke, will it?
John Bert!
Bert I were only asking.
Alfred Let's see if we can walk. How's that?
Jim Not bad. It's jolly kind of you. (*He groans with pain again*)
John Where we taking him to?
Roberta We'll take him home with us. Mother will know what to do. You lead the way Peter.
Jim (*as they exit*) What are your names? My name is Jim.

Peter leading the way, they all exit

Perks changes the points and the set changes to the cottage

Mother is weeding in the garden

Peter rushes in

Peter Oh Mother—we've found a hound in a red jersey in the tunnel and he's broken his leg and they're bringing him home.
Mother They ought to take him to a vet. I really can't have a lame dog here.
Peter He's not a dog really, he's a boy.
Mother Then he ought to be taken home to his mother.
Peter He's living in at the grammar school. Oh Mother, you must be nice to him. I told him I was sure you'd want us to bring him home. You always want to help everybody.

All the children enter, with Jim

Mother Well—what have we here?
Roberta Hello, Mother.
Jim I'm Jim.
Mother Hello, Jim. So you have a broken leg?
Jim I think so.

Mother That won't do, will it? Phyl—can you run down and fetch Dr Forrest?
Phyllis Yes, Mother.

Phyllis exits

Mother And we must put Jim to bed and make him as comfortable as possible.
Jim Oh I do hate to be such trouble. (*He groans again*)
Mother Don't be silly, you're no trouble at all. Bring him through here, boys.

Jim is carried into the house

Perks And their mam put him to bed—the same bed where the Russian gentlemen had stayed.
Mother Lift him gently. That's it. Be careful.
Phyllis Oh, do be careful!
Jim I think I'm going to faint again!
Perks But he didn't faint. And soon, with a large mug of hot, sweet tea in his hand he were quite cheery.
Mother His mother died when he was only a baby. His father lives in Northumberland but he does have a grandfather who lives quite near here. We must get in touch with him. And the headmaster of his school. We must do that at once.

The Doctor arrives at the door

Doctor More problems?
Mother Hello, Doctor. It's this poor young fellow here. We think he's broken his leg.
Doctor Has he now? That won't do at all, will it. Now, I'm afraid you'll all have to leave the room apart from your mother.
Mother (*to the Perks' children*) And I think you'd better be going home anyway. Your mother and father will wonder where you've got to.

The Perks' children go

Peter, Roberta and Phyllis take themselves off into the garden while the Doctor sees to Jim

Peter I wish doctors weren't so stuck up about who they'll have in the room when they're doing things. I should most awfully like to see a leg set. I believe the bones crack like anything.
Phyllis
Roberta } (*together*) Don't.
Peter Oh don't be so feeble. You say you want to be Red Cross Nurses yet you can't even stand hearing me say about bones crunching. You'd have heard them crunch on the field of battle.
Roberta Stop it!
Peter Cowards!
Roberta We're not cowards.

Jim cries out

Peter There—that was a bone crunching.
Roberta Peter!
Phyllis You're horrid!
Peter Girls!

The Lights fade to a spot on Perks downstage

The Doctor exits

Perks And right soon Jim's legs were set and he were quite, quite comfortable. All this excitement had helped take Bobbie's mind off her poor dad locked up in prison for summat he never did. Each day she waited to receive a reply from the old gentleman. Then—after the third day—she had the biggest surprise in store she could ever have imagined. They were playing in the attic room. They heard a knock on the kitchen door downstairs, some voices, then their mam called upstairs.

The Lights come up on Mother at the breakfast table with the Old Gentleman

Mother (*calling*) Children—Jim's grandfather has arrived. Hurry, he wants to see you.

The children rush in

Roberta Hello.
Peter Jim will be pleased.
Old Gentleman Hello, children.
Children Hello!
Peter Well I never. How do you do.
Phyllis It's our own old gentleman!!
Mother Phyllis!
Old Gentleman That's all right.
Phyllis I'm so awfully glad it is you.
Roberta When you think of the lots of old gentlemen there are in the world—it might have been almost anyone.
Peter I say though, you're not going to take Jim away now are you?
Old Gentleman Not at present.
Peter Oh spiffing! We're becoming ever such good friends and it's much more fun talking to a boy.
Mother Peter.
Peter Well it is.
Old Gentleman Your mother has kindly agreed to let him stay here.
Peter Oh terrific!
Old Gentleman I thought of sending a nurse but your mother is good enough to say that she'll nurse him herself.
Peter But what about her writing? There won't be anything for him to eat if Mother doesn't write.
Mother That's no problem, Peter.
Peter Why?

Old Gentleman Shall I tell them our little arrangement?

Mother Certainly.

Old Gentleman Your mother has consented to give up writing for a little while and to become matron of my hospital.

Phyllis Oh, and shall we have to go away from Three Chimneys and the railway and everything?

Mother No, no darling.

Old Gentleman The hospital is called Three Chimneys Hospital and my unlucky Jim's the only patient.

Peter Ohhh!

Old Gentleman So you'll all be staying here for quite some time ... unless something very wonderful happens. Now—I must go—I hope to come back tomorrow to visit Jim again if that's all right.

Mother Of course it is. You're welcome any time.

Old Gentleman And thank you so much for caring for my grandson.

Mother It's a pleasure.

Old Gentleman Take care of your mother, my dears. She's a woman in a million.

Roberta Yes, isn't she?

Old Gentleman God bless you all. Will Bobbie come with me to the gate?

Roberta Of course.

Roberta and the Old Gentleman move into the garden

Old Gentleman You're a good child, my dear, and I received your letter ...

Roberta Oh.

Old Gentleman But it wasn't needed. When I read about your father's case in the paper at the time I had my doubts. And ever since I've known who you were I've been trying to find out things. I haven't done very much yet, but I have hopes, my dear—I have hopes.

Roberta Oh?

Old Gentleman Yes—I may say great hopes. But keep your secret a little longer. Wouldn't do to upset your mother with a false hope, would it?

Roberta Oh—but it isn't false. I *know* you can do it. I knew you could when I wrote. You don't think Father did it, do you? Oh say you don't think he did!

Old Gentleman My dear, I'm perfectly certain he didn't. Now goodbye— and keep your fingers crossed.

Roberta Oh I'll keep every one of my fingers crossed.

The Old Gentleman exits

Perks The next few weeks rolled by right quickly. They all became good friends with Jim and their mam spent much more time with 'em than ever before. She read to 'em wrote funny little verses for 'em. And me?—well I never saw eye nor hair of 'em from one week to the next, 'cept when I called on them.

Phyllis and Peter go into the garden

Phyllis I wonder if the railway misses us. We never go to see it now.

Roberta It seems ungrateful, we loved it so when we hadn't anyone to play with.

Peter Mr Perks is always coming up to ask after Jim and we sometimes see John and Alfred and the others.

Phyllis The thing I don't like is not waving to the ten fifteen and sending our love to Father on it.

Peter Well look (*taking out the gold watch*), let's go down to it now—we should just catch it.

Roberta What a good idea.

Peter Come on then!

The children exit

Perks turns the points and the set changes to outside the tunnel

As the children enter Phyllis stops to tie her bootlaces

Hurry up or we shall miss it.

Phyllis I can't hurry, my bootlace has come undone again.

Peter When you're married your bootlace will come undone going up the church aisle and the man that you're marrying will tumble over it and smash his nose on the flagstones and then you'll say you won't marry him and you'll have to be an old maid.

Phyllis I shan't. I'd much rather marry a man with a nose smashed in than not marry anybody.

Roberta All the same it would be horrid to marry a man with a smashed nose because he wouldn't be able to smell the flowers at the wedding. Wouldn't that be awful?

An approaching train is heard

Peter Bother the flowers at the wedding! Listen, the train's arriving. Come on!

Roberta (*waving*) Take our love to Father!

Peter ⎫
Phyllis ⎭ (*together*) Take our love to Father.

Roberta Our old gentleman is waving.

Peter Everyone's waving.

Roberta Well!

Peter Well!

Phyllis Well!

Roberta What on earth does that mean?

Phyllis I don't know.

Roberta Perhaps the old gentleman told the people at his station to look out for us and wave.

Peter It's most extraordinarily rum!

Roberta But why would he do that?

Phyllis I don't know.

Roberta And didn't you think there was something different about the old gentleman's wave today?

Peter ⎰ (*together*) No.
Phyllis ⎱

Roberta I do. I thought he was trying to explain something to us with his paper.

Peter Explain what?

Roberta I don't know, but I do feel most awfully funny. I feel just exactly as if something is going to happen.

Peter I'll tell you what's going to happen—Phyllis's bootlace is going to come undone again.

Phyllis Horrid boy!

Phyllis hits Peter and runs away

Peter (*chasing*) Wait till I catch you!

Peter runs off

Perks turns the points and the set changes to the station

Perks And she did feel funny an' all. Couldn't settle all day. She just knew summat was going to happen if you know what I mean. Couldn't settle to nothing. Couldn't read. Couldn't write. Couldn't even sit in the garden. Finally in the afternoon, she decided she'd walk down to the station. In the village everyone she passed was smiling and waving and were ever so friendly. She just couldn't understand it.

Roberta walks to the station

A man and a woman pass by

Woman God bless you, love. You'd better hurry though, it's nearly quarter past three.

Man Good luck to you, love. We're all happy for you.

Perks Now then Bobbie. So you've heard.

Roberta Heard what?

Perks This. (*He holds up a newspaper*)

Roberta I don't understand.

Perks When I read about it in here this morning I don't think I've been more pleased in me entire life.

Roberta Read what, Mr Perks?

Mrs Perks enters with all the Perks' children

Mrs Perks Oh Bobbie—we're all so happy for you. Aren't we?

Children Yeah we are.

Roberta Why? I don't understand. What are you all talking about?

Perks Here it comes now. Bang on time. The three twenty express from London.

Perks blows his whistle as the train arrives and halts. A door slams. Steam hisses

Good luck, miss!

Roberta's father enters with a suitcase

Roberta Daddy!! Oh my Daddy!

Roberta and her father embrace

Peter, Phyllis and Mother come into the station and all embrace

CURTAIN

FURNITURE AND PROPERTY LIST

Three main sets are required: the station; the Three Chimneys Cottage and garden; the countryside and tunnel. Either a revolve, trucks or a composite setting can be used depending on facilities available. Please read the Author's Note on page v.

Fixed area: railway points downstage

Moveable areas: station, cottage and garden, countryside and tunnel

ACT I

STATION
On stage: Waiting-room
Benches
Double doors leading to the platform
Ticket office

Off stage: Suitcases (**Mother**)

Personal: **Perks:** whistle and pocket-watch (used throughout)

COTTAGE AND GARDEN (Page 2)
On stage: Living-room:
Sideboard
Table. On it: 3 candles and a box of matches
Fireplace. In it: coal-shovel, poker
2 chests with lids. Inside first: tablecloth; cutlery; candles; willow-pattern teacups and saucers and plates wrapped in paper; sardines; biscuits; preserved ginger; raisins; candied peel; marmalade; ginger wine. On second: tray of food covered with tea towel
Bedroom:
Bed. On it: bedclothes, etc.
Trunk. In it: men's clothing, including a nightshirt
Garden:
Bench

STATION (Page 6)
Set: Ticket collector's hat for **Perks**

Off stage: Shopping (**Mrs Walker**)

COTTAGE AND GARDEN (Page 13)
Strike: 2 chests and contents and candles, etc.

Set: Food, cutlery, etc., pens, papers on table
Shilling on sideboard

Off stage: Bag (**Doctor**)

Personal **Doctor:** list

OUTSIDE THE TUNNEL (Page 16)

On Stage: Tree (collapsible), strawberry plants, etc.

Off stage: Large white sheet with words: LOOK OUT AT THE STATION **(Peter and Phyl)**

STATION (Page 16)
Personal: **Roberta:** note

COTTAGE AND GARDEN (Page 18)
Strike: Items from table

Off stage: Hamper containing various items including roses, letter, peaches, chicken, port wine **(Perks)**

Personal: **Perks:** sweetbriar in hat

OUTSIDE THE TUNNEL (Page 20)
Off stage: Large white sheet with words: SHE IS NEARLY WELL THANK YOU **(Peter and Phyl)**

COTTAGE AND GARDEN (Page 20)
Strike: Hamper and contents

STATION (Page 21)
On stage: As before

COTTAGE AND GARDEN (Page 25)
Set: Chair and flowers in garden
Meat laid on table

Off stage: Tray of food **(Roberta)**
basket containing sandwiches **(Mother)**

OUTSIDE THE TUNNEL (Page 28)
Personal: **Roberta:** detachable white petticoat

ACT II

STATION (Page 32)
Personal: **District Superintendent:** three gold pocket-watches

COTTAGE AND GARDEN (Page 35)
Set: Washing line, pegs, basket of washing (clothes worn by **Mr Szczepansky** previously)

STATION (Page 38)
Off stage: Pram containing the following wrapped in newspaper: children's clothes, gooseberries, shovel, honey, bootlaces, meat, garden produce, decorations, buns **(Roberta, Peter** and **Phyl)**

Personal: **Phyllis:** brooch
          Mrs Perks: wrapped tobacco, handkerchief

          COTTAGE AND GARDEN (Page 46)
Set: Knitting (for **Mother**)

Personal: **Roberta:** newspaper cutting

          OUTSIDE THE TUNNEL (Page 48)
Personal: **Roberta:** newspaper cutting, letter, envelope

          INSIDE THE TUNNEL (Page 49)
Personal: **Peter:** bag containing candle, matches, milk in a container

          COTTAGE AND GARDEN (Page 52)
Set: Garden trowel (for **Mother**)

Off stage: Bag **(Doctor)**

Personal: **Peter:** gold pocket-watch

          OUTSIDE THE TUNNEL (Page 56)
On stage: As before

          STATION (Page 57)
Off stage: Suitcase **(Father)**

Personal: **Perks:** newspaper

LIGHTING PLOT

ACT I

To open: Back lighting to create silhouette

Cue 1   **Perks** comes through doors   (Page 1)
Bring up night effect on exterior of station

Cue 2   **Perks** turns the set to the cottage setting   (Page 2)
Crossfade to night effect outside cottage

Cue 3   **Mother** lights a candle   (Page 3)
Bring up dim, flickering effect in cottage

Cue 4   The **children** exit carrying the candle; **Mother** lights another   (Page 3)
candle
Fade and bring up lights to reflect natural sources

Cue 5   **Mother** lights another candle   (Page 3)
Increase lighting

Cue 6   The **children** enter   (Page 4)
Increase lighting further

Cue 7   The **children** light candles   (Page 5)
Increase lighting again

Cue 8   **Perks** moves set to the station setting   (Page 6)
Bright morning light

Cue 9   **Perks** moves set to the cottage setting   (Page 13)
*Localized interior lighting on cottage; exterior general lighting
on garden*

Cue 10   **Perks** moves set to the tunnel setting   (Page 16)
Exterior general lighting

Cue 11   **Perks** moves set to the station setting   (Page 16)
General lighting

Cue 12   **Perks** moves set to the cottage setting   (Page 18)
Localize lighting on cottage interior

Cue 13   **Perks** moves set to the tunnel setting   (Page 20)
Exterior general lighting

Cue 14   **Perks** moves set to the cottage setting   (Page 20)
Interior lighting

Cue 15   **Perks** moves set to the station setting   (Page 21)
General lighting

Cue 16   **Perks** moves set to the cottage setting   (Page 25)
Interior lighting

Cue 17	**Mother** "Yes." *Crossfade to spot on* **Perks** *downstage*	(Page 27)
Cue 18	**Perks:** "Then Phyllis had a good idea." *Crossfade to cottage garden; daytime*	(Page 27)
Cue 19	**Phyl:** "Yes, Mother." *Crossfade to spot on* **Perks** *then crossfade to dusk effect on tunnel exterior*	(Page 28)
Cue 20	**Bert:** "I can see it coming!" *Train lights from tunnel, gradually approaching, at its most intense when squealing brakes signal train's stop*	(Page 30)
Cue 21	**Bobbie** faints. Train engine continues to idle *Fade to black-out*	(Page 31)

ACT II

To open: General lighting on station

Cue 22	**Perks** moves set to the cottage *Bright exterior lighting on garden*	(Page 35)
Cue 23	**Perks** moves set to the station *Crossfade to general daylight on station*	(Page 38)
Cue 24	**Perks** moves set to the cottage *Crossfade to interior evening effect in cottage*	(Page 46)
Cue 25	**Roberta:** "I'll try, Mother, but it won't be easy." *Crossfade to spot on* **Perks** *then bring up bright daylight on tunnel exterior*	(Page 47)
Cue 26	**Perks** changes set to interior of tunnel *Fade to spill of light on* **children** *on edge of set*	(Page 49)
Cue 27	**Peter** lights a candle *Slightly increase lighting*	(Page 50)
Cue 28	Train passes, candle goes out *Snap out lighting*	(Page 51)
Cue 29	**Peter** lights the candle *Bring up lighting to level of Cue 27*	(Page 51)
Cue 30	The **children** exit *Crossfade to spot on* **Perks** *then bring up general lighting on garden and cottage*	(Page 52)
Cue 31	**Peter:** "Girls!" *Crossfade to spot on* **Perks** *downstage*	(Page 54)
Cue 32	**Perks:** ". . . then their mam called upstairs." *Bring up bright morning effect on cottage and garden*	(Page 54)
Cue 33	**Perks** turns set to the tunnel *Bright, exterior lighting*	(Page 56)
Cue 34	**Perks** turns set to the station *Crossfade to general afternoon effect*	(Page 57)

EFFECTS PLOT

ACT I

Cue 17	**Perkins** blows his whistle again *Train moves out, noises off*	(Page 22)
Cue 18	**Mother:** "Yes." *Train engine*	(Page 27)
Cue 19	**Phyl:** "... I'm still hungry." *Creaking*	(Page 29)
Cue 20	**Roberta:** "That tree's going to fall!" *Tree falls, creaking stops*	(Page 29)
Cue 21	**John:** "Ssshhhush!" *Distant train approaches, getting louder and louder as script*	(Page 30)
Cue 22	**Roberta:** "It won't stop!" *Train very close, steam hisses, wind blows, brakes squeal, at end of squeal, noise of train idling continues*	(Page 31)
Cue 23	**Roberta** faints, lights fade to black-out *Fade engine sound*	(Page 31)

ACT II

Cue 24	**Perks** changes the set to the tunnel interior *Train approaches*	(Page 49)
Cue 25	Children enter tunnel *Dripping water, effect of echo of voices as script*	(Page 50)
Cue 26	**Alfred:** "It's a train." *Train approaching*	(Page 50)
Cue 27	**Bert:** "Eh, isn't this exciting?" *Train passes and goes away, steam etc.*	(Page 51)
Cue 28	**Roberta:** "Wouldn't that be awful?" *Train approaches and passes*	(Page 56)
Cue 29	**Perks:** "The three twenty express from London." *Train approaches and halts. Single door slam. Steam*	(Page 57)

MADE AND PRINTED IN GREAT BRITAIN BY
LATIMER TREND & COMPANY LTD PLYMOUTH
MADE IN ENGLAND